A IS FOR ARAB

ARCHIVING STEREOTYPES IN U.S. POPULAR CULTURE

THE JACK G. SHAHEEN ARCHIVE AT TAMIMENT LIBRARY &
ROBERT F. WAGNER LABOR ARCHIVES, NEW YORK UNIVERSITY

An Archives Project and Publication of the
Asian/Pacific/American Institute, NYU

An Archives Project and Publication of the Asian/Pacific/American Institute, NYU
The A/P/A Institute brings together accomplished scholars, community builders, and artists
from New York City and beyond in interactive forums, reflection, and new research.

Co-editors: John Kuo Wei Tchen and Amita Manghnani

Editing + Production Manager: Laura Chen-Schultz

Design + Layout: Kiku + Marlene Yamaguchi/BabyAlpaca Design

Photographs: GION STUDIO

Editorial Production: Judy Susman, James G. Cantres, Ona Lu

Printed by GHP Media

Contents

5   **Imaging Arab America: A Dialogue with Jack Shaheen**
Ella Shohat

9   **Jack Shaheen: A Philosopher/Journalist**
Ali Mirsepassi

15   **"A is for Arab"**
Jack G. Shaheen

59   **Beyond 9/11: Engaging with the Jack G. Shaheen Archive**
Amita Manghnani

63   **The Re-Education of Jack Shaheen:
Why the Shaheen Collection Is Important & What You Can Do to Help**
John Kuo Wei Tchen

66   **Endnotes**

68   **Jack G. Shaheen Publications**

69   **Selected Bibliography**

71   **Acknowledgments**

Imaging Arab America: A Dialogue with Jack Shaheen

Ella Shohat

I first became aware of Jack Shaheen's significant work in the early 1980s, when I was writing my doctoral dissertation on the representation of Arabs and Palestinians in Israeli cinema, examining the links and the analogies to American cinema's representation of colonized spaces, and more specifically its imaging of the Orient. When Shaheen's book *The TV Arab* was published, I was euphoric to discover scholarly work focusing specifically on the stereotypes of Arabs in the media. In 1985, I used his book (along with Edward Said's *Orientalism*) as one of the key texts in my course on Orientalism in American Cinema. In 1987, I received a moving letter from Jack, in response to my essay "The Return of the Repressed: The 'Palestinian Wave' in Recent Israeli Cinema." Those were very lonely days for the few of us doing this work, and his encouraging, sympathetic words were very meaningful. Since then, I have come to appreciate his tremendous generosity and hospitality as a person.

Jack Shaheen has played at least three very important roles: as a scholar of seminal texts on Arab representations; as an activist shrewdly negotiating with the powerful institutions that control such representations; and finally, as an archivist who has gathered together the fundamental corpus of works concerning Arabs in the cinema. If I had had the Jack G. Shaheen Archive available to me then, it would have significantly facilitated my research. The archive, especially in its exploration

of films from the turn of the century, makes clear that American cinema *began* with Orientalist imagery. *The Dance of Fatima* (1887), one of the first silent films, showcased a belly dancer who had come to the U.S. as part of the Columbian exposition. (Some years later, in my essay "'Coming to America:' Reflections On Hair and Memory Loss," the section "In Search of Fatima" partly reflected on this forgotten but seminal moment in the history of representing the "Orient" across the Atlantic.) The history of American cinema, as Shaheen's work demonstrates, is inseparable from the history of Orientalism and the "coming" of Arabs to the Americas. By excavating this buried history of the cinematic Arab, Shaheen's work has inspired generations of scholars and writers.

I have been deeply appreciative of Shaheen's work on stereo-types. Studying stereotyping processes and practices in popular culture as well as studying the repeated and pernicious constellations of character traits are vital to understanding hegemonic representations. Stereotype analysis, despite certain theoretical limitations, has performed an invaluable public service by revealing oppressive patterns of prejudice that, at first glance, might have appeared random or inchoate. Stereotype analysis a la Shaheen sheds light on the psychic devastation inflicted by systematically negative portrayals on those groups assaulted by them, whether through the internalization of stereotypes themselves or through the negative effects of their dissemination. Analyses of stereotypes, further, have demonstrated that stereotypes are not an error of perception but rather a form of social control. Shaheen's work, in this sense, has proved invaluable for the ongoing research on media portrayals of the Middle East and its diasporas. My work has been very much concerned with the same sociopolitcal issues, even if I have deployed different methodological tools, highlighting discourse analysis, narrative structure, focalization, recurrent tropes, etc.

In a series of publications, "Gender in Hollywood's Orient" (1990); "The Trouble with Hanna: Costa Gavras and the Representation of Palestine" (with Richard Porton, 1984); *Israeli Cinema: East/ West and the Politics of Representation* (1989); "Gender and the Culture of Empire" (1991); and *Unthinking Eurocentrism: Multiculturalism and the Media* (with Robert Stam, 1994), I explored Orientalism in popular culture as symptomatic of the colonialist imaginary. Edward Said's and Jack Shaheen's texts have demonstrated the important links between the situation in the Middle East and the images of Arabs reflected in the American media. My work continued to study Orientalism in American popular culture, while highlighting the analogies (and dis-analogies) between the representation of Arabs in American and in Israeli cinemas, especially between images of Native Americans and Palestinians on the one hand, and Blacks and Arab-Jews/ Mizrahim on the other. Orientalist narratives, I suggested, could simultaneously deploy a positive image of "the Arab" and yet remain Orientalist in their ideological perspective and discursive framework. Sometimes, even the image of the "good Arab" is not exactly good when one probes closely the ideological dimension of the narrative. The image of the "good Arab," furthermore, can mask Orientalist perspectives.

My work has thus dialogued with the analyses of the deleterious effects and historic roots of Orientalist stereotyping in the media. I have sought especially to underscore the crucial role of sexual difference within the culture of empire. Hegemonic Western representation has been imbricated in a series of Eurocentric articulations of power. Identifying the structural analogies between the representations of disparate colonized spaces allows us to see how imperial narratives are in fact organized around metaphors of rape, fantasies of rescue, and eroticized geographies. "Gender in Hollywood's Orient," points to the multiple sub-genres within Hollywood's films, as well as to the symbiotic relationship between patriarchal and colonial articulations of difference. In this way, I have tried to extend Shaheen's invaluable work in order to address the intersections of imperial and gender discourses.

For these and many other reasons, the donation of the Jack G. Shaheen Archive to NYU is an enormous gift to all of us scholars whose work on representations, stereotypes, and Orientalism has been shaped by his groundbreaking studies. Moreover, his gift affords us the opportunity to re-think the very idea of "the archive." Rather than merely being what the state happens to own and the documents that the government has produced, "the archive" is also a rich trove of audiovisual artifacts, television programs, and films, that forms an invaluable source for historians of popular culture and for scholars of cinema, media, and visual culture.

Aladdin and His Lamp, *1952, film poster.*

Aladdin and His Lamp, *1952, film poster.*

Jack Shaheen: A Philosopher/Journalist

Ali Mirsepassi

Professor Jack Shaheen engages the broader public in conversation on the fundamental cultural issues of our time. He brings to mind what Michel Foucault called the philosopher/journalist: there is intellectual responsibility for turning the specific everyday happenings into multiple stories, like light interacting with each drop to create the rainbow. Scholars and intellectuals, the later Foucault argued, need to tell the stories of the governed and those denied a voice. I feel Jack Shaheen embodies the philosopher/journalist of our time. He is certainly the most prolific scholar researching the cultural representation of Arabs and Muslims in the U.S. and the West generally. His work, in this context, is a critique of the American popular production/consumption of images and ideas which through "entertainment" — a power instrument often more subtle than open propaganda — inflicts pain and dehumanizes the Muslim and Arab "other." Shaheen writes from the point of view of the struggling immigrant community finding its place in an open and changing, yet painfully challenging, America over generations. His is the world of Lebanese immigrants finding their way in the multi-cultural lifeworld of the steel city of Clairton, Pennsylvania, in the early 1920s, with all of the interacting everyday ethics of these diverse peoples (Greeks, Italians, Lebanese, and Serbians).

As a philosopher/journalist, Shaheen has theorized the fundamental danger linking technology, the imagination, and identity-targeting violence. One can argue that Shaheen's works have the power of a truth-teller to reveal to the public that "entertainment" that uses artistically-imagined scapegoats runs the high risk of inflicting injuries upon millions of others. It can perhaps even pave the way for popular acceptance of acts of violence and war. This is a highly difficult message to convey concerning the culture of one's country, and even more difficult to accept. Through evidence from popular culture, Shaheen has demonstrated how the creative power of the entertainment/media industries can produce dehumanizing images of Arabs and Muslims — and reduce them to a single imaginary entity. Shaheen's work documents how imaginative tendencies become embedded in a culture; how over several generations it becomes an imaginative legacy (representations). The fundamental resource is brute technology: it reduces the amassed and open plurality of representations to discursively closed homogeneous representations (set narratives), as mass-circulated films, television shows, newspapers, comic books, toys, games, novels, and magazines create naturalized ideas about entire peoples and religions. Identity-targeting violence, in its apparent contingence, is significantly produced by these invisible imaginative bodies, which function sometimes manipulatively through larger patterns of national policy and agendas.

Shaheen's works, books, documentaries, and public lectures have three very important qualities: 1) He is meticulous in presenting the empirical evidence. His vast research on Hollywood movie archives and other media materials provide a tremendous cultural-imaginary terrain to work upon; 2) His style of writing and speaking invokes a humanist and "ethical politics" which teaches and inspires human goodness while avoiding demonization of the humanity of those he criticizes; 3) He is very skillful in communicating with his audience about sensitive and politically-charged issues (terrorism, the 9/11 tragedy, ethnic and religious prejudice) in a manner suited for creating more hopeful and ethical horizons for thinking and being. For Shaheen, being in the world today involves cultivating a broad and cosmopolitan vision of care for the "other," where critical engagement over justice defends those who are excluded, silenced, or violated at the local level. As a construction of cosmopolitanism, it is down-to-earth in being inclusive of multiple cultural ideas and practices rather than being the universal imposition of one form of imaginary at the expense of all other forms of being and thinking.

Globalization means that on the structural level, we are forced to care passionately about a geographically distant place; yet short of either living there or having extended family one must imagine it through shared public channels. This simple material fact underlies the profound phenomenological significance of a media-dominated society (in cinematic terms, America first went to war in Iraq in the 1943 action movie *Adventure in Iraq*). Shaheen's work, on a rudimentary level, provides a historical record of the portrayals of Arabs and Muslims in U.S. popular culture and media from the late-19th century to the present. But the discursive body has its own unique history of qualitative development and ruptures (i.e., after the Holocaust, the construction of Jews as lecherous murderers or greedy financiers became less publically tolerable). Behind everyday objects (Halloween costumes, popular films, toys, and children's cartoons) there is a hidden imaginative-topographical history helping to shape the perceptual lives of generations across various constructed divides. Research

into understanding this problem of non-innocence or an unconscious imaginative reservoir conditioning everyday events — but linked to broad economic issues such as the global energy crisis — is what Shaheen has done for most of his life, and we have learned much from his life-long dedication to the scholarly vocation. His work has combined practical research into everyday experience with theoretical models of power and imaginative representation in modern democratic societies. It is wonderful that Shaheen's critical scholarship is neither a hostile nor cynical condemnation of America's entertainment industry or even the contemporary Western attitude toward Arabs and Muslims. His caring and gracious humanism is manifest in his works, articles, documentaries, and public lectures — all inspiring and emotionally empowering ways of telling the truth about a contemporary humanity which he encourages to expand in order to include all people and cultures.

Shaheen's deep ethical commitment as a public intellectual engaged in cross-cultural understanding has communicated political optimism as well as identifying the complex and unseen dangers of reproducing images. Through his work we see the daily interaction of the imagined, unseen and systemically forgotten, upon an everyday cultural terrain which witnessed the trajectory from the mid-1960s civil rights movement to the American election of President Barack Obama — a memorably rapid historical cultural-popular shift away from politically poisonous stereotypical imaginaries to more open humanist horizons. Shaheen approaches his critical work with little personal or intellectual bitterness, moral arrogance, or intellectual superiority. His humanist sensibilities and unique storytelling style is distant from the spirit of hostile or violent criticism: it merely lays bare the reality of how Hollywood's image making and fantastic films produce heroes and villains in our real-life experiences — and documents the emotional, psychological, and physical impact of these created villains upon the flesh and blood people they purport, unjustly, to represent.

The New Yorker, *July 26, 1993, magazine cover.*

11

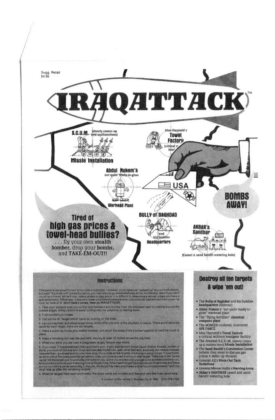

IraqAttack game, 1991.

Riteway advertisement, ca. 1970s.

Come to savage seething Arabia on a terror search for forbidden treasures of the ages!

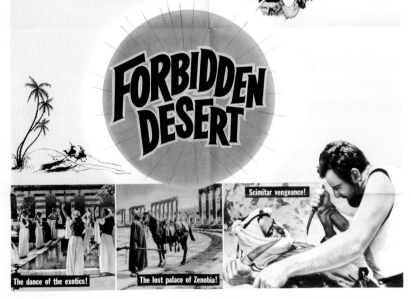

Forbidden Desert, *1957, film poster.*

"A is for Arab"

Jack G. Shaheen

The subtlest and most pervasive of all influences are those which create and maintain the repertory of stereotypes. We are told about the world before we see it. We imagine most things before we experience them.... We are all captives of the picture in our head. **— Walter Lippmann**[1]

Introduction Degrading images of Arabs are a slanderous aspect of popular culture's history; they have been virtually unchallenged for more than a century. As a rule, Arab women have been projected as mostly mute and submissive figures: belly dancers, bundles in black, and beasts of burden. Arab men surface as villains: Bedouin bandits, sinister sheikhs, buffoons, and gun wielding "terrorists."

We have Europe to thank for the origin of these stereotypes. The European translations of the epic fantasy book *One Thousand and One Nights* have had a profound impact on perceptions of Arabs and Muslims in the West. The first such translation (into French) was made in the 18th century by Antoine Galland. Interestingly, the original Arabic versions of *One Thousand and One Nights* were not nearly as influential as the European editions. Explains Rutgers Professor Charles Haberl, "Galland and his European successors made up many of the stories; they also turned European folk tales into 'Arabian' ones by employing stock 'Oriental' themes and imagery." These tales featured characters such as Aladdin, Sinbad, and Ali Baba living in a mythical Arabland populated by genies, sultans, wicked viziers, exotic harem maidens, magic lamps, and flying carpets. What matters here, says Haberl, "is that the European versions were translated back into Arabic, Persian, and other languages, and went on to acquire a far greater credibility than the original *Arabian Nights*. This is the ultimate example of Europeans inscribing their fantasies upon the Middle East: the very quintessence of Orientalism."[2]

Anti-Arab and anti-Muslim prejudice have a long and powerful history. Explains Edward Said in his seminal book, *Orientalism*, "The imaginative examination of things Oriental was based more or less exclusively upon a Western consciousness out of whose unchallenged centrality an Oriental world emerged, first according to general ideas, about who and what was an Oriental, then according to a detailed logic governed not simply by empirical reality but by a battery of desires, repressions, investments, and projections." Early on, in the 18th and 19th centuries, European artists and writers began presenting ongoing fictional renditions of the wild Oriental

The Sheik, *1921, film poster.*

The Sheik (1921) and *The Son of the Sheik* (1929) helped solidify several enduring myths: Arab men dominate women, Arab women are subservient harem-dwellers, and the only good Arab is the Western hero (e.g., Rudolph Valentino in *The Sheik*) clad in Arab garb.

Musk, Hashish and Blood, *1951, paperback book.*

Arab women have been projected as mostly mute and submissive figures: belly dancers, bundles in black, and beasts of burden. Hector France's book, a collection of tales of a Frenchman "among the cruel men and passionate women of Algiers," abounds with imagery of the sexualized Arab woman.

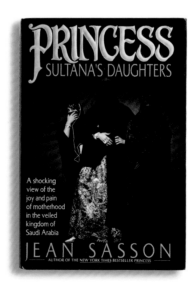

Princess Sultana's Daughters, *2001, paperback book.*

More contemporary works of fiction like Jean Sasson's *Princess Sultana's Daughters*, *Princess Sultana's Circle*, and *Princess* exploit the stereotype of the submissive, sexualized Arab woman. In Sasson's trilogy, the women of the Saudi royal family are oppressed by Arab male chauvinism despite their elite status.

WILLIAM FOX
PRESENTS
TOM MIX
IN ARABIA

Tom Mix in Arabia, *1922, film still.*

Arab men surface as villains. Popular American Western film star Tom Mix is
held captive by a band of Arabs. In his films, Mix often portrays a clean-cut hero
cowboy in contrast to the rampant, violent hoards of villains he encounters.

Other — the desert-dwelling, lazy, bearded Arab surrounded by concubines who were auctioned off at slave markets. Writes Said, "The perverted sheikh can often be seen snarling at the captured Western hero and blonde girl . . . [and saying] 'My men are going to kill you, but they like to amuse themselves first.'" Later on, points out Said, America's purveyors of popular culture inherited and embellished Europe's pre-existing Arab caricatures[3], which were both phobic (the Other was an object of fear and repulsion) and philic (the Other was an object of fascination and attraction) expressions.

Included here are over 50 visuals of Arabs. These are part of the Jack G. Shaheen Archive, my collection of more than 4,000 items that is housed at New York University's Tamiment Library & Robert F. Wagner Labor Archives. For nearly four decades, I have researched and collected memorabilia that capture U.S. popular depictions of Arabs. I give special emphasis to entertainment images, including those found in television programs, films, comic books and comic strips, movie stills and posters, print advertisements, toys and games, editorial cartoons, novels, and other ephemera. The archive's extensive film collection — more than 1,100 feature films — reveals Hollywood's evolving attitudes toward the Arab people; it includes silent movies dating from the early 1900s, dramas, documentaries, comedies, and children's cartoons. Also among the collectibles are magazines, film scripts, essays, correspondence, and notes that I maintained for my lectures, articles, books, television appearances, and other projects.

When viewing the materials in the archive, a telling reality persists: lurid and insidious Arab portraits are staple fare. The Arab-as-villain motif is present throughout the entire history of Arab images in U.S. popular culture. Subsequently, over time, these pervasive, persistent images helped create and enforce prejudicial attitudes toward Islam, Arabs, and Muslims, resulting in a narrow view of the Arab and specific U.S. domestic and international policies. Over the years, the absence of positive, realistic images has also helped nurture suspicion and prejudice. As a result, inaccurate and demonizing images of the Arab have been with us for more than a century, impacting everyone from children to teens to adults.

The Arab-as-enemy image was prevalent long before Operation Desert Storm (1991), the U.S.'s first war with an Arab country, the War in Iraq (2003–2011), a conflict in which more than 4,000 American soldiers and 200,000 Iraqis died and countless others were seriously injured, and before September 11, 2001, when 19 Al-Qaeda terrorists killed nearly 3,000 Americans. In 1976, the movie *Network* pounded home the myth that the Arabs were "medieval fanatics [who are] simply buying us." The Arabs, warns the film's protagonist, "are going to own what you read and what you see. . . . Hell, they already own half of England," he declares. Even more startling is the 1943 film *Adventure in Iraq*, which features the U.S. Air Force staging a "shock and awe" bombing of Iraq's pro-Nazi "devil worshipers" — 48 years before the U.S. actually entered into war with Iraq. In the film, Iraq's ruling Sheikh Ahmid favors an alliance with Germany, boasting he is negotiating oil rights with Hitler. In the end, all ends well. U.S. fighters drop bombs on Iraq's "primitive" inhabitants. Ahmid is defeated; his American hostages are freed.

No individual, no nation should cast judgment on an entire race, culture, nation, or religion based on the heinous acts of some fanatics. Yet, after 9/11 some of us attributed the actions of the lunatic fringe to the vast majority of peaceful Arabs and Muslims, falling into the stale trap — "seen one, seen 'em all."

For those readers who may have difficulty distinguishing between Arabs and Muslims, allow me to explain. The term "Arab" is essentially a linguistic category referring to about 300 million people — 14 million are Christians — from 22 Arabic-speaking countries. "Muslim" is a religious category, referring to 1.4 billion Muslims, most of whom are Indonesian, Indian, and Malaysian.[4]

The fanatics who attacked the U.S. on September 11, 2001 no more represent Muslims than the Ku Klux Klan represents Christians. No matter. Since 9/11, hate crimes directed at American Muslims and Americans with Arab roots shot up by more than 1,600 percent. Those who looked "Arab" were subjected to vicious stereotyping and incidents of violence. The FBI said they investigated about 1,000 hate crimes and acts of violence directed at Arab Americans, Muslim Americans, South Asian Americans, and other people perceived to be of Middle Eastern origin.[5] Members of these communities were singled out, harassed, detained, and deported. Some were tagged "camel jockeys," "terrorists," and "rag heads." Just four

Yankee Pasha, *1954, film poster.*

Arabland is populated by genies, sultans, wicked viziers, exotic harem maidens, magic lamps, and flying carpets. In *Yankee Pasha*, the American heroine Roxana is kidnapped and sold to a Moroccan Sultan. Her lover Jason ventures to Morocco to save her and is gifted Lilith, a maiden whom he exchanges for Roxana to win her release. The term "pasha" is an Ottoman honorific equivalent to the English "lord," but this film takes place in Morocco, which was never under Ottoman rule even at its largest extent. Multiple realities are conflated into one simplistic notion of Arab, Muslim, or Ottoman.

Time, *July 2, 1979, editorial cartoon.*

Though there are five non-Arab members (Angola, Ecuador, Iran, Nigeria, and Venezuela) in the Organization of Petroleum Exporting Countries (OPEC), cartoonists represented OPEC as a sheikh, suggesting the dominant role Arab nations held in the cartel and thus in the control of worldwide oil reserves. In the 1970s, as gas prices rose, images of decadent Arab oil sheikhs proliferated in editorial cartoons. Exaggerated noses and dark beards marked the images as distinctly anti-Semitic.

days after the 9/11 attacks, Francisco Silva Roque gunned down Balbir Singh Sodhi in Mesa, Arizona. Roque assumed Sodhi was an Arab because he wore a turban (Sodhi was actually an Indian Sikh). When the police arrested Roque, he protested, claiming the shooting was an act of patriotism. He purportedly shouted, "I'm an American. Arrest me and let those Terrorists run wild?"[6] In the years after 9/11, 16 people of the Sikh faith have been killed in the U.S. in religious hate crimes.[7]

No stereotype exists in a vacuum; history teaches us that when a people are continuously vilified there are serious social, political, and human consequences. Consider both the demonization of Germany's Jews as "evil" prior to World War II, which led to the deaths of six million Jews, and the vilification of Americans with Japanese roots, which brought about the incarceration of more than 100,000 loyal American citizens and residents during the second World War.

For decades, the Arab stereotype has effectively poisoned minds, implying that Arabs are our enemy. To paraphrase Plato, those who tell the stories rule society. Perceptions impact public opinion, which in turn impact policies, which in turn bring about conflicts between nations, resulting in destruction and death. This damaging Arab-as-enemy myth may have helped expedite our involvement in our recent two wars.

Beginnings   One reason I decided to collect and write about Arab images in U.S. popular culture was because I wanted to shelter children, especially those with Arab roots. Guiding me was the traditional proverb, "One generation plants a tree. The tree's branches shade those of the next generation."

I recall, still, a hot, humid morning in mid-August 1973. Our children Michael and Michele were watching Saturday morning cartoons. Suddenly, they ran up the stairs and rushed into my arms. "Daddy, Daddy," they cried, "there are some bad Arabs on TV." At the time, my children were only five and six years old, and it was scary for them to watch their favorite cartoon heroes — Donald Duck, Tintin, Bugs Bunny, and Porky Pig — beat up Arab evil-doers. It was a very disturbing experience, similar to walking into those

Arabian Nights, *1977, comic book.*

Based on a many-centuries collection of Middle Eastern and South Asian stories, the first English language version appeared in 1706. This version, most often called *Arabian Nights*, is set in a mythical Arabland. Editing out actual places, peoples, languages, and religions (besides Islam, which not all Arabs practice), these simplified versions of the stories homogenize and caricature entire regions. The Marvel Comics version of *Arabian Nights* is among dozens of films, cartoons, and comic books that have been inspired by *Arabian Nights* and its characters Aladdin, Sinbad, Scheherazade, and Ali Baba.

Gauge Master Arms Anti-Iraq Gun Club Target, *1990.*

Despite the nine Arab nations fighting alongside the American military in the Coalition forces during the first Gulf War, anti-Arab sentiment intensified during this period. On the home front U.S.A., Iraqis and the larger Arab world were all portrayed as enemies rather than as allies.

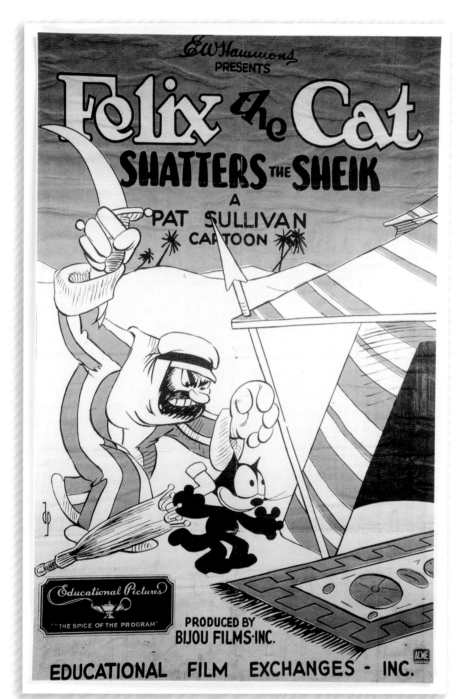

Felix the Cat Shatters the Sheik,
1926, film poster.

A spoof of *The Sheik* (1921), this black and white film followed Felix the Cat's journey to the Arabian Desert to sell umbrellas. Here Felix tries to escape an Arab villain.

mirrored rooms at amusement parks in which all you see are distorted images of yourself. In the years ahead, Michele and Michael helped with my research, calling to my attention scores of Saturday morning cartoons showing bad Arabs prowling the screen. Cartoons like *Laverne and Shirley* and *Heckle and Jeckle* featured villains like Ali Boo-Boo, the Desert Rat, and Sheik Ha-Mean-ie, an Arab intent on conquering the U.S. and the world.

That same year, we went shopping for Halloween masks at a Spencer's gift store in a mall in Fairview Heights, Illinois. Prominently displayed alongside the usual array of goblin, demon, and vampire masks was an ugly Arab mask, complete with grotesque facial features. The chain stocked no other masks representing other ethnic or racial groups. A few days later, eight students participated in Michael and Michele's Catholic school's annual Halloween parade dressed up as bearded, stereotypical "Arabs," carrying oil cans and bags filled with fake money. Their friends' Arab costumes impacted Michael and Michele; they decided not to wear traditional Arab garb at the school's ethnic festival later that year. Weeks later, when a story in *Scholastic* magazine equated Palestinians with terrorists, a few classmates harassed my children, questioning their roots. They came running home, asking, "Are we Palestinian or Lebanese?" "Neither," I said, "you're both Americans. But, you have roots in both countries. Your mother has Palestinian roots; mine are Lebanese." "But that's hard to explain to our friends; we just need one word," my children responded. So, Michael came up with "Lebastinian." Michele opted for the more romantic, "Palanese."

My children's ongoing exposure to prejudice helped me realize that I had to do *something*. They and other Arab Americans were growing up without ever having seen a humane Arab in a children's cartoon — not one to look up to or cheer on. To them, it seemed easier for a camel to go through the eye of a needle than for a TV Arab to appear as a genuine human being. Whatever happened, they must have wondered, to Aladdin's good genie?

That was nearly 40 years ago. Their "Daddy, Daddy" cries altered my life. At the time, I taught Mass Communications at Southern Illinois University at Edwardsville (SIUE). My primary media classes were Broadcast Writing, Documentary Film, and Broadcast Management. On the research front, I had established myself as a media critic, successfully publishing essays on the role of public broadcasting and a book on nuclear war films.

In 1975, two years after that morning in August, I delivered my first lecture on the Arab stereotype at the American University of Beirut (AUB). Following my time at the AUB as a Fulbright professor, I began to seriously examine racial and ethnic stereotypes in general, and, specifically Arab images on American network and public television channels. The research process began with *TV Guide*. Each and every week I would peruse the magazine, reading summaries of upcoming programs and looking for names of Arab characters in TV wrestling matches, dramas (*Mission Impossible*, *The Rockford Files*), comedies (*Alice, Sonny and Cher*), children's and teens shows (*The Hardy Boys, Fantasy Island*), documentaries (*The Saudis, The Palestinians*), and specials.

When I found a program with Arab characters and/or Arab settings I would record the episode using my VCR and take notes about the role Arab characters played — what they said and what was said and done to them. I remember watching the Dr. Seuss *Pontoffel Pock, Where Are You?* animated special, which takes place in the mythical kingdom of Cashmopolis. Here, Pock falls for Neefa Feefa, "the greatest eyeball dancer in the world," who is held hostage by the sultan of Cashmopolis. After Neefa sings a song of remorse, lamenting, "How I hate working for this slob," the fat Arab sultan locks her in a tower in the middle of the desert. In the end, heroic Pock frees Neefa from the desert tower within which she is imprisoned, liberating her from the toothless sultan's clutches. This was representative of much of what I viewed on television in the 1970s — from TV dramas to documentaries to comedies to children's cartoons.

By 1976, I had gathered information on about 40 episodes featuring Arab characters as the enemy. When I submitted my research proposal, the first ever to examine television's Arabs, to SIUE, I was confident I would receive support. If my proposal was accepted, I would teach one less class, giving me more time to write. I would also receive funds to purchase videos, so I could continue to tape and study selected episodes.

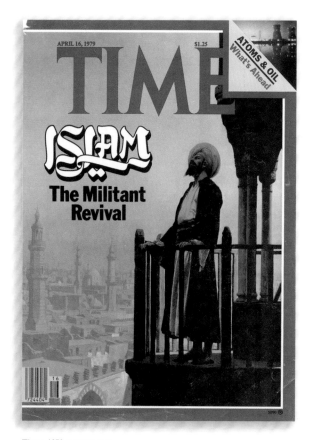

Time, *1979, magazine cover.*

This *Time* cover depicts a *muezzin* calling Muslims to prayer from the minaret of a mosque with the title, "Islam: the Militant Revival," conflating notions of Islamic faith and military action. Viewers are led to believe that there are intimate connections between Muslim spirituality and militancy.

Unexpectedly, however, the academic support that I had always earned with my non-Arab related projects promptly dissipated. The School of Fine Arts committee placed my request at the bottom of the pile. So did the Graduate School's Research and Projects committee. When I asked both committee chairpersons "Why," they were mum. Finally, one evening a committee member approached me in the men's room, of all places, and whispered that my proposal was rejected because some committee members considered it "Arab propaganda." I was taken aback by this comment and by the fact that I was being tagged the "Arab" professor. Still, I continued seeking research support, though not one request was ever approved. Later, a few people came out of the closet and became vocal. "Why are you defending the Arabs?" detractors would ask me. Even a gracious elderly woman at our church questioned my interests, "Why, Jack, are you defending the Muslims?"

These comments hurt. I had never before, in or out of the classroom, experienced any prejudice. Instead, my colleagues would compliment me on my research skills; it did not matter to them where my parents came from. Each and every football season they fondly tagged me "Steeler Jack" because I was such an enthusiastic born-and-bred Pittsburgh Steelers fan. I was as American as apple pie, or so I thought. Later, the "Arab Professor" tag followed me to Flint, Michigan; here I spoke to a large, enthusiastic audience at Mott Community College about the dangers of *all* stereotypes. Yet, the headline in the local newspaper began with, "Arab Professor."

Regrettably, unlike words like "Irish" or "Italian," to many, the word "Arab" has a derogatory meaning. Nowadays, "Arab" is employed to help advance the sinister stereotype: Arab=Muslim=Evil Enemy Other. The word "Arab" is almost never used as a complimentary or even neutral term. How have Arab Americans learned this lesson? I came to realize that while our nation has thousands of wonderful Middle Eastern restaurants, no restaurant dares call itself an "Arab Table" restaurant, like popular Greek Table and Italian Table restaurants. Think about it. Would you rather dine at O'Leary's Irish Grill or at Abdullah's Arab Table? I have never seen references to Arab fusion; not even Arab kabobs or Arab yogurt on menus. Never. Would you prefer to say "pass the Arab yogurt" or "pass the Greek yogurt;" "pass the Arab bread" or "pass the pita?" My Ph.D. work had earned me a position in academia, but now I was beginning another kind of educational journey.

In retrospect, the discrediting of my research motivated me to move forward. During the summer of 1975, I completed my first article on stereotypical portrayals of Arabs, which documented television's images of Arabs. During a three-year period, from 1975–1978, I received more than 50 rejection letters from publications unwilling to publish the article.

The most memorable came from Harriet Van Horne, editor of *Television Quarterly: The Journal of the National Television Academy of Arts and Sciences.* She refused to print the essay, she said, because it was too well written! Writes Ms. Horne in her January 12, 1977 letter: "Dear Professor Shaheen, You have written a most interesting piece on 'TV's Distorted Image of the Arab' but . . . the *Quarterly* simply cannot plunge into ethnic controversies. Were we to publish this, we'd be obliged to publish pieces — probably not as good or as sane as yours, about TV's distorted views of [other groups]. We'd also have to run a rebuttal from some special interest group saying that the TV picture of Arabs was not distorted. You can appreciate, I am sure, what problems would be set in motion by our publishing this essay." Ms. Horne was clearly more concerned about having to reject essays calling attention to problematic stereotypes of other groups and receiving complaints from "special interest groups," than she was about publishing a ground-breaking essay.

Finally, in 1978, my article appeared in the *Christian Century* and in the *Wall Street Journal.* And, in 1984, dozens of letters of rejection later, my first book, *The TV Arab*, hit bookshelves. The book is based on eight years of television viewing and offers analysis of over 200 episodes of network entertainment shows, cartoons, and documentaries featuring Arabs.

Given the obstacles I encountered, why continue investigating Arab images? Was it because I wanted to prove to my colleagues that my research was legitimate and not "propaganda?" Was I outraged because I seldom read or

The Atlantic, *September 1990, magazine cover.*

In the cover story "The Roots of Muslim Rage," Bernard Lewis charges fundamentalist Muslims with deep-seated resentment of the Western world, based on the notion that the ideal separation between church and state is essentially American, rendering "the West" "enemies of God." Though Lewis attempts, ineffectively, to qualify his statements to a small group during a certain cyclic moment in time, the *Atlantic* headline conveys a different message.

The Book of Sounds ABC, *1979, children's book.*

Alongside an alligator, apple, and arrow, an Arab is depicted as representing the letter "A." Children learning the alphabet are exposed very early to imagery of Arabs as angry and threatening. The ax attached to the Arab's belt, drawn oddly in a Western hatchet style, suggests violence.

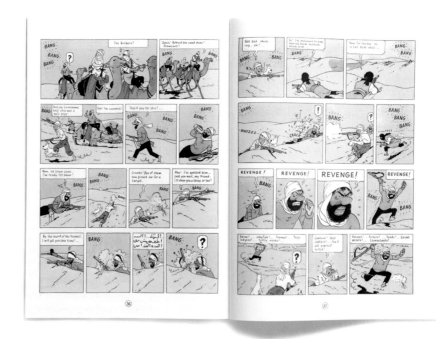

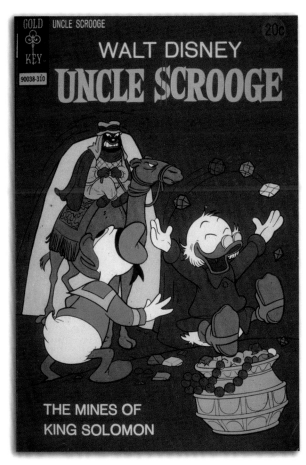

(top) Uncle Scrooge: The Mines of King Solomon, *1973, comic book.*

(left) The Adventures of Tintin: The Crab with the Golden Claws, *1941, children's book.*

Arabs are vilified in children's comics as they are shown here staring menacingly at favorite cartoon characters, Donald Duck and Tintin.

Dennis the Menace, *1979, comic strip.*

In Hank Ketcham's tongue-in-cheek style we can glean anti-Arab sentiment in everyday American life.

Halloween mask, ca. 1990s.
Available in Halloween costume shops, this anti-Semitic caricature mask was stocked alongside the usual array of goblin, demon, and zombie masks.

Aim High Be Kind to Animals t-shirt, 1990.
This t-shirt was purchased at the Marine Command and Staff College Bookstore. Anti-Arab "target practice" is advocated, while playing with the rhetoric of animal rights activists.

saw anything that depicted the Arab as a regular guy? Or, was it because I wanted to be the first scholar to examine this issue in-depth? Surprisingly, not being able to locate literature on the Arab image was helpful to my own intellectual process. I was obliged to conduct extensive research on other groups victimized by harmful images. I found the Arab stereotype to be somewhat similar to other stereotypes. During the early days of filmmaking, for example, Hollywood almost always projected heroic white American Christians defeating non-white (e.g., Native American, Asian, and Black) villains who were intent on killing and raping fair-complexioned heroines. In films like D.W. Griffith's *Battle at Elderbush Gulch* (1913), dog-eating savage Native Americans attack peace-loving townsfolk, scalping a woman alive; and in Griffith's *Birth of a Nation* (1915), Ku Klux Klan members are saviors who bring down uncivilized, ruthless, drunken blacks trying to rule the country. In George Melford's *The Sheik* (1921), Arabs auction off women in slave markets and an ugly, obese sheikh tries to rape the English heroine. And the 1923 movie-serial *The Mystery of Fu Manchu* spawned a host of Yellow Peril movies, which featured sneaky, lecherous Asians doing dastardly deeds in opium dens. These images provided a comparative framework within which to analyze the stereotypical images of Arabs that I was collecting.

I forged ahead to investigate Arab images because of family — the values and ideals that were upheld by loved ones who had emigrated from Lebanon to the steel city of Clairton, Pennsylvania in the early 1920s. From them, I learned about responsibility and compassion. Their love enabled me to become more aware and sensitive to hurtful images. By their example, I learned never to vilify others and to accept people as they are, no matter color, creed, or culture. My earliest lessons about acceptance began around our kitchen table. I would watch our neighbors — Greeks, Italians, Serbians, and our Lebanese cousins — chat in thick accents as they drank Maxwell House coffee and munched on fresh loaves of freshly baked Syrian bread covered in butter.

My mother Nazara, a real movie buff, worked part-time in our local theater's cashier booth. There was one major source of screen images then, the State Theater, where as

Honest Abdul's Oil Well, *1979, board game.*

From the mid-1970s through the mid-1980s wealthy Arabs were
regularly targeted in novelty items produced for children. The
accompanying booklet explained that as sheikh, children were
"entitled to as many wives as you care to have."

PRIVILEGES
and
RESPONSIBILITIES
OF OWNING AN
OIL WELL

One
Authentic
Oil Well

How to Beat Those High Gas Prices, *ca. 1970s, board game.*

Similar to the oil well game, this game depicts Arabs as greedy and exploitative, intent on destroying the American economy. This wealthy, oil sheikh image endured for decades.

The Enemy of Rambo: S.A.V.A.G.E. Nomad, *1981, figurine.*

This Nomad toy is cast as the enemy of Rambo, the fictional American Vietnam War veteran and star vehicle for Sylvester Stallone. As described on the packaging, Nomad is "Devious, Traitorous and Desperate. The Desert is his only home." He conducts "terrorist assaults on innocent villages," according to the manufacturers, who packaged the action figurine with an assortment of weapons. With protests organized by the American-Arab Anti-Discrimination Committee, Coleco Industries ceased production of the figurine.

a youngster I was lucky enough to gain free admittance; later I became an usher. Back in the 1940s, war and Tarzan movies as well as Cowboy and Indian shoot-em-ups were popular. Tarzan movies were teaching us that Africans and African Americans, like reel Native Americans, weren't civilized. But whenever I mimicked or mocked Native Americans, my mother would caution me. She said that ridiculing others damaged the imagination. "Have compassion for all people, Jackie," she would say. "Accept people as they are, and not as they appear in films." Though we never discussed reel Arab images, I remember wincing as I watched my favorite comedians, Laurel and Hardy, Abbott and Costello, and the Three Stooges, beat up and ridicule dense Arabs. Laurel and Hardy ridicule Arabs in *Beau Hunks* (1931), the Stooges trounce them in shorts like *Three Arabian Nuts* (1943) and *Malice in the Palace* (1949). Abbott and Costello sock it to them in films such as *Abbott and Costello in the Foreign Legion* (1950) and *Abbott and Costello Meet the Mummy* (1955). Fast forward to the 1970s. Now, Michael and Michele wince while seeing the identical Stooges shorts, as well as Laurel and Hardy and Abbott and Costello movies on TV.

Films last forever.

Representative examples from the collection I began acquiring Arab collectibles in the mid-1970s. I couldn't resist collecting all these stereotypical items — from placemats to figurines to romance novels. I found them everywhere — in flea markets, toy shops, comic bookstores, and on eBay. Collecting served as a much needed break from my rigorous writing routine. Over time, hundreds of Arab collectibles had nearly filled up our three-bedroom home. That is, until New York University expressed an interest in acquiring and making accessible my Arab memorabilia. Taken together, these collectibles reveal the pervasive nature of the stereotype, which continues to corrupt the minds of millions of people, here and abroad.

Decades ago, noted journalist Edward R. Murrow cautioned us about the sins of omission and commission, pointing out that what we do not see is as important, if not more important than what we do see.[8] The overwhelming majority of Arab collectibles presented here offer distorted portraits of Arabs. Omitted, for the most part, is Arab humanity; items fail to show Arabs as they are, as ordinary people. The damaging stereotype is fixed: Arab men are stripped of their masculinity; Arab women are stripped of their femininity. At times, some Arab men are hyper-masculine in their domination of women; and some Arab women are hyper-feminine in their passivity. What's important to keep in mind is that together — Arab men, women, children, families, and nationalities — are stripped of their humanity. Across genres, this unwavering stereotype is as solid as granite. Repetitive images of sameness prevail: the evil TV Arab is the villainous Movie Arab is the abominable Book Arab is the gross Marketing Arab is the unacceptable Theatrical Play Arab is the dreadful Toys and Games Arab is the atrocious Comic Book Arab, and on and on it goes. Our ability to recognize and examine harmful past portraits should enable us to avoid repeating them in the future and also help bring about their eventual demise.

TOYS AND GAMES From the mid-1970s through the mid-1980s, wealthy Arabs were regularly targeted in novelty items produced for children. At a fashionable gift shop in Washington, DC, I paid $6.00 for a model oil well called "Honest Abdul's Miniature Oil Well," featuring a leering, lecherous sheikh named "Honest Abdul." The instructions booklet describes the daily routine of an oil sheikh — gambling, drinking, and lounging in ostentatious homes complete with private harems. "You are now entitled to as many wives as you care to have," the booklet proclaims. I also came across the Cracked's Oil Sheik Game (1980) which offers young readers a chance to find out "what it takes to become an oil sheik" by playing "The Oil Sheik Game." The rules are similar to Monopoly, but these playing cards display scimitars, oil wells, and faces of scowling Arabs on the $10 to $100 billion bills. The object of the game: "Gain control of the oil-producing nations." To make the game "more life-like," novice players are advised "to wrap a pillow-case around your head. If you are ugly, put your head in the pillow-case." Also among the tips: "Impress Arabs with your patriotism by dating a camel." When a player passes Mecca he receives "$50 billion."

My collection does not yet include many combat video games, which are growing in popularity; 69 percent of

Cracked's Oil Sheik Game, *1980, board game.*
This board game encourages players to impersonate Arab "sheiks" by amassing $10 to $100 billion bills and game pieces representing scimitars, oil wells, and oil-producing nations. To really inhabit the role, the game advises wrapping "a pillow-case around your head."

Circuit's Edge, *1989, computer game.* **Conflict,** *ca. 1988, computer game.* **The President is Missing,** *1988, computer game.*

Numerous computer games promote similar anti-Arab themes: the Arab as America's enemy and the Middle East as a hotbed of terrorist activity. These games, all released in the late-1980s, played heavily on the adversarial image of Arabs cultivated throughout the previous decade.

Big Chief Wahoo and the Magic Lamp, *1940, children's book.* **Blaze Brandon with the Foreign Legion,** *1928, children's book.* **Captain Midnight and Sheik Jomak Khan,** *1946, children's book.* **Mickey Mouse and the Sacred Jewel,** *1936, children's book.* **Mickey Mouse and the Magic Lamp,** *1942, children's book.* **Tom Mix and His Circus On the Barbary Coast,** *1940, children's book.*

These illustrated children's books introduce young readers to stereotypes about the Arab World -- Tom Mix and Captain Midnight square off against uncivilized Arab villains and the mysteries of the Orient fascinate Mickey Mouse and Big Chief Wahoo (whose character also reinforces racist ideas about Native Americans).

American heads of households play video and computer games; the average age of video game players is 37 years old.[9] The few I've come across — *Conflict* (1988), *F-19 Stealth Fighter* (1988), *Enemy Engaged* (2000), *CIA Operative-Solo Missions* (2001), and *Call of Duty 4: Modern Warfare* (2007) — feature scores of Arab villains, such as *Call of Duty 4's* Khaled Al-Asad, from nations like Yemen, Iraq, Libya, and Lebanon.

LITTLE BIG BOOKS These illustrated books were popular children's fare from the mid-1930s through the mid-1940s and include *Mickey Mouse and the Sacred Jewel* (1936*), Blaze Brandon with the Foreign Legion* (1938), *Tom Mix at the Circus on the Barbary Coast* (1940), and *Captain Midnight and Sheik Jomak Khan* (1946). The action occurs in mythical kingdoms like "Genieland," "Stumbool," and "Raghbagh." Here, rulers like "Evil Prince Kashdown" reject Arab harem maidens, preferring to woo Western women. Islam is vilified. Arabs appear as uncivilized beings. In *Blaze Brandon with the Foreign Legion*, barbaric Bedouins massacre legionnaires: "Never would he [Blaze] forget the roaring waves of blood-thirsty Moslems, their bearded faces twisted in hate, their curved sabers reaching upwards."[10] In the end, Western heroes and Native Americans bring down deceitful Arabs and Muslims. Slurs abound: Arabs are tagged "dolts," "dopes," "as treacherous as . . . snake[s]," "hawk-faced," "numb-brained jackal[s]," "a bunch of cutthroats," "blood-thirsty Moslems," and "sons of peegs." These books and others reinforced the notion that Arabs are awful people. The impressions one is exposed to at an early age are often the most difficult to shake.

CARTOONS Off and on for decades, our favorite cartoon characters, such as Bugs Bunny and Woody Woodpecker — see *A Lad and His Lamp* (1929), *A-Lad-in-Bagdad* (1938), *A-Lad-in His Lamp* (1948), and *A Lad in Baghdad* (1968) — routinely beat up Arabs. One representative sample: Mickey Mouse trounces Arabs in Walt Disney's 1932 cartoon *Mickey in Arabia*. In the mid-1980s, a colleague called my attention to this 1932 cartoon. But how to see it; Disney hadn't yet released it on video. So, for assistance, I called on my friend, Casey Kasem. Casey, a well-known radio personality and the voice of Shaggy in the animated Scooby-Doo series, was well-respected in the industry.

The Return of Tarzan: Fury in the Desert!,
1973, comic book.

Just one of more than 200 comic books in the Jack G. Shaheen
Archive featuring Arab villains, *The Return of Tarzan* pits the
heroic feral child against the threat of Arabs. The early books
in Edgar Rice Burrough's *Tarzan* series depicted Arabs as
dangerous enemies and this characterization persisted through
later books, comic books, comic strips, and films.

Life with Archie: The Scourge of the Sahara,
1978, comic book.

Even Archie has to fend off treacherous saber-wielding Arabs! While on
a trip to the land of "Aladdin and the Arabian Nights," he encounters
the Scourge of the Sahara, despite the fact that the Sahara Desert is
in North Africa, not on the Arabian Peninsula. The comic conflates the
entire Arab world with one location, the Arabia of ancient myth.

Mark Hazzard: Merc, *1987, comic book.*

In comic book series such as *Mark Hazzard*, Arabs are the primary
enemy of fearless American heroes.

The Iron Sheik, *1984, figurine.*

Hossein Khosrow Ali Vazir, known professionally as The Iron Sheik, was a famous wrestler with the World Wrestling Federation from 1983–88 (other "Arab" wrestlers of the period include Palestina the Syrian Terrorist and Akbar the Great). Vazir also used the ring names Colonel Mustafa and The Great Hossein Arab, even though he was Iranian and not Arab. The names of his finishing moves, the "Camel Clutch" and the "Iranian Drop," play on some of the most common associations ascribed to the Middle East.

Casey asked a Disney vice-president for a helping hand and immediately the executive arranged a private screening for us in a posh theater on the Disney lot. The stereotypes were so offensive that when *Mickey in Arabia* ended, we just sat there, shocked into a temporary silence. Finally, en route back to my hotel where I was attending a Children's Television Programming conference, Casey thanked me for calling his attention to the cartoon, saying I could always count on his help when contesting stereotypes.

I regularly came across other Saturday morning cartoons which displayed animated Arabs as villains. I recall, especially, a 1990s "Demon Quest" episode from *Batman, the Animated Series* (telecast on the Fox Children's Network, May 4, 1993). Here, evil Arabs wearing headdresses surface in the Sahara as allies of Ra's al Ghul, an "alien" plotting to rule the world. Enter Batman: he brings down scores of dark-complexioned Arabs armed with sabers and rifles. Several months after the "Demon" segment was telecast, I contacted my friend Casey for assistance. We met with Fox programmers in Los Angeles to discuss the episode. We asked programmers to consider writing and telecasting a fresh episode, one showing Arabs helping Batman trounce some generic villains. Unfortunately, this time around, even with Casey Kasem at my side, our concerns fell on deaf ears.

COMIC BOOKS My collection contains more than 200 comic books featuring Arab villains — the sinister sheikh, the repulsive terrorist, and the rapacious bandit. Once again, the prevailing theme is Arab as enemy. A few examples: Tarzan beats up an Arab chieftain who abducts Jane, Superman foils Arab terrorists who hijack a U.S. nuclear carrier, and the Fantastic Four capture a hideous oil sheikh. Always opposing the hero, Arabs are depicted attacking Batman, Superman, Archie, Tarzan, Americans, Israelis, Europeans, and human decency. Arabs are tagged as "desert devils," "mountain goats," and "bandits in bed sheets." The 1981 comic book *Mickey Mouse Joins the Foreign Legion* is based on a 1936 comic strip with the same title. Here, Mickey prevents the scheming bandit chief Yussuf Aiper from ambushing the legionnaires by outwitting Yussuf and his 250 gun-toting bandits.

TV WRESTLING Since the mid-1960s, Arab villains have appeared in the great American morality play — professional wrestling. For a half-century, fans have booed and hissed a host of keffiyeh-clad baddies: Akbar the Great (aka Skandor Akbar), The Sheik (aka The Sheik of Araby, The Original Sheik), Abdullah the Butcher (aka The Madman from Sudan), Muhammad "Camel Clutch" Hassan, The Iron Sheik (aka The Great Hossein Arab), and Palestina (the Syrian Terrorist). Patriotic Americans triumph in the end, pinning those evil Arab foreigners. The Arab portrayals are somewhat different from the portrayals of other villains in professional wrestling,

due to their consistency and longevity — over the course of 50 years, never has an "Arab" wrestler ever been portrayed as a hero or patriot.

MOTION PICTURES In my book *Reel Bad Arabs: How Hollywood Vilifies a People*, I discuss over a thousand pre-9/11 films — from *Fatima* (1896) to *Ali Baba and the Forty Thieves (*1944) to *True Lies* (1994*)* to *The Mummy Returns* (2001) — that include Arab characters or references. I began working on the book in the early 1980s, thinking it would be finished in a few years after I identified 200 or so movies with Arab characters. But as soon as I located one film, others appeared. The list of films, thanks to several comprehensive computer searches and assistance from friends who kept directing my attention to less obvious movies, kept growing and growing. At the time, many movies were not readily available on DVD or online; Netflix, Hulu, and YouTube did not exist. In order to see old classics, I was obliged to visit research institutions all over the country — from Madison, WI to New York City; from Los Angeles to Washington, DC. At the Library of Congress, I perused nearly every film review that had ever been published, searching for movies with Arab names or settings. Alone, I watched nearly all of the films, over and over again. I wanted to be certain my research was fair and accurate. Finally, after 20 years of writing about and viewing more than 1,000 pre-9/11 movies, the book was published in 2001.

Ali Baba and the Forty Thieves,
1944, film poster.

This 1944 film stands in stark contrast to typical Hollywood portrayals of Arabs. Here, Ali Baba and his 40 thieves are portrayed as heroic Arabs that rob the rich and care for the poor. Interestingly, this film includes an actual historical event, the 13th century Mongolian siege of Baghdad.

Abbott and Costello Meet the Mummy, *1955, film poster.*

Abbott and Costello in Lost in a Harem, *1944, film poster.*

Historically, movies featuring comedians such as Abbott and Costello, Laurel and Hardy, the Three Stooges, and others, portray Arabs as subjects of ridicule.

True Lies, 1994, film still.

During his research, Shaheen found that many pre-2001 films projected Arabs and Muslims as Public Enemy #1. This 1994 anti-Palestinian film was produced with support from the U.S. Department of Defense and the U.S. Marine Corps Aviation. In this still, Art Malik (playing Palestinian terrorist Salim Abu Aziz) is shown holding Jamie Lee Curtis hostage while Arnold Schwarzenegger is handcuffed, unable to rescue her. *True Lies* reinforced many Arab stereotypes as Palestinians appeared as a demonic, despicable people.

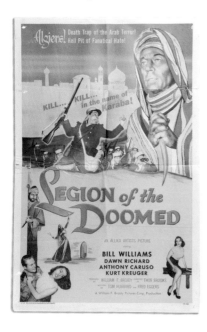

Legion of the Doomed, 1958, film poster.

Among the many films which portray the experiences of the French Foreign Legion in the Middle East, *Legion of the Doomed* showcases the trials and tribulations of French soldiers in the "lawless, hateful" land of Algeria. Algeria and its people, and by extension the Muslim world, are described as having "a great past but no future."

I found that Hollywood's Arabs were almost always portrayed as violent and uncivilized beings. The vast majority of reel villains were Palestinians, Egyptians, sheikhs, and Arab women. In addition, about 300 films that had nothing whatsoever to do with Arabs displayed gratuitous slurs and scenes that demeaned Arabs. Only around 14 films offered positive depictions and 54 were neutral. All the other films were negative: many projected Arabs and Muslims as subhuman and as Public Enemy #1. Movies were creating stereotypes and presenting fantasy as reality.

One film that was particularly disturbing was Disney's *Aladdin* (1992), which opened with the lyrics:

> Oh I come from a land,
> From a faraway place
> Where the caravan camels roam
> Where they cut off you ear,
> If they don't like your face,
> It's barbaric, but hey, it's home.

For months, I, along with Albert Mokhiber, the President of the American-Arab Anti-Discrimination Committee, made dozens of phone calls and wrote numerous letters requesting a meeting with Disney CEO Michael Eisner to discuss *Aladdin*'s stereotypical lyrics and images. Disney responded to our concerns with yawns of indifference until I asked Casey Kasem to intervene once again. Eventually, the three of us — Casey, Albert, and I — met with Disney executives Richard Cook and Terry Press. As soon as we entered the conference room, the meeting got off to a sour start. Cook and Press blamed us for all the "bad publicity" the studio was receiving. To some extent, they were right. When *Aladdin* was released, I was lecturing throughout the U.S. and Canada. Reporters attending my lectures wrote articles about my criticisms of *Aladdin*'s stereotypes. I encouraged reporters to call Disney to get the studio's side of the story. And most of them did in fact call Disney, only to be met with silence.

To help change the direction of the meeting, I slammed my hand on the table and slowly began handing Cook and Press copies of all the letters we had sent to Disney requesting a meeting. "Don't you think the 'bad' press is your fault?" I said. "Why didn't you have the courtesy to respond to any of our letters?" Suddenly, the tone of the meeting changed. Though Press and Cook said no film edits were possible, they agreed to consider changing *Aladdin*'s opening song's lyrics for the video release of the film.

Months later, "Where they cut off your ear, If they don't like your face," was deleted from the video and DVD version of *Aladdin*. A July 14, 1993, *New York Times* editorial complained that merely changing one line from the opening lyrics was not enough. "To characterize an entire region with this sort of tongue-in-cheek bigotry, especially in a movie aimed at children, borders on the barbaric."[11] And, regrettably, two years after Disney's *Aladdin* was released, the video sequel, *The Return of Jafar* (1994), popped up on TV screens, complete with offensive lyrics:

> Arabian Nights like Arabian Days . . . they shock
>   and amaze.
> Pack your shield, pack your sword,
> You won't ever get bored,
> Though beaten and gored, you might.

On a positive note, according to some Disney executives our meeting helped the studio avoid the same kind of stereotyping with *Pocahontas* (1995), though some would argue that this film, too, is incredibly problematic. Yet, *Pocahontas'* director, Mike Gabriel, affirms that from the very beginning, the image of Native Americans "was a clear concern since we had been blasted by Arab [American] groups for defamatory lyrics in 1992's *Aladdin*."[12]

NEWS MEDIA One enduring theme in print and broadcast news is that Arabs and Muslims are a threat to us. In December 1977, CBS-TV's *60 Minutes* featured Morley Safer in "The Arabs Are Coming," a segment warning viewers that Arabs were invading and buying up chunks of America. Fast forward to November 19, 1990: the cover of the *National Review* displays scruffy Arabs on camels with this warning, "The Muslims Are Coming." Fast forward to 2005: The Clarion Fund, a pro-Israel non-profit whose "documentaries" have been accused of fostering hatred against Muslims, financed and released *Obsession: Radical Islam's War Against the West*. This film merits our attention because of its pervasiveness, Islamophobic message, and political implications. Throughout *Obsession*, viewers see

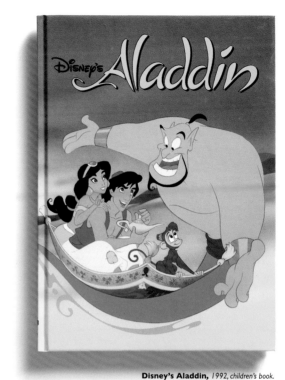

Disney's Aladdin, *1992, children's book.*

In 1992, *Aladdin* was released and opened with song lyrics that claimed "they cut off you ear, If they don't like your face, It's barbaric, but hey, it's home." Protests followed, resulting in Disney cutting a lyric line.

Disney's Aladdin, *1992, children's book.*

In this striking image, Jasmine, Aladdin's love interest, is shackled by Jafar, Disney's racialized depiction of a lecherous antagonist. He orders a shackled Jasmine to bring him more wine, epitomizing the misogynist stereotypes so prevalent with regard to Arab men.

"THE MUSLIMS ARE COMING! THE MUSLIMS ARE COMING!"
The National Review, *1990, magazine cover.*

This *National Review* cover perpetuates anti-Arab and anti-Muslim hysteria. Referencing, unsuccessfully, the gentle anti-Cold War Norman Jewison film *The Russians are Coming, the Russians are Coming* (1966), this cover and essay by Daniel Pipes within are simply xenophobic. With the dissolution of the Soviet Union and the reunification of Germany, many Cold War rivalries and tensions subsided, allowing for Arabs and Muslims to be targeted as new enemies in American political consciousness.

scores of fanatical Muslims threatening to bring down Western civilization. Shockingly, the Fund managed to convince dozens of major newspapers throughout the country to distribute 28 million copies of *Obsession* free of charge. The DVDs were inserted into over 70 newspapers, predominantly in swing states before the 2008 presidential election; only five newspapers refused to distribute the DVD.

The Clarion Fund is the same group that is behind the 72-minute propaganda film *The Third Jihad*, which was screened before 1,500 New York City police officers as part of an anti-terrorist training initiative. *The Third Jihad's* narrator tells viewers that Muslims in the U.S. are a threat; that most mainstream Muslim groups are not moderate, rather "if you look a little closer you'll see a very different reality. One of their primary tactics is deception."[13] The film hammers home the myth that Islam and terrorism are synonymous. For example, viewers witness a black and white flag, denoted as the flag of Islam, flying over the White House.

New York City Mayor Mike Bloomberg has strongly condemned the film, but he also said he doubts that *The Third Jihad's* negative images influenced any of the city's police officials. Yet, the film's message that Muslims are trying to take over the U.S. is a dangerous one. Consider the impact of the pervasive anti-Arab and Islamophobic rhetoric and images that exist in our society — the furor over plans to build an Islamic center in downtown Manhattan, politicians using the fear of Islam as a political weapon to gain votes, the deportation of immigrants, the vandalism of mosques around the country, and the myth that the practice of Islam, in and of itself, is a precursor to terrorism. It would be a step in the right direction if the Mayor would initiate programs which would contest and counter the threatening stereotypes presented in *The Third Jihad* and other media.[14]

ROMANCE NOVELS, THRILLERS, and OTHER BOOKS One enduring narrative found in hundreds of Harlequin Sheikh and Desert Love romance books, which include titles like *The Sheik's Reward* and *Possessed by the Sheik,* is a love story between an exotic, Arab sheikh and a Western woman. Points out specialist Jessica Taylor, "The sheikh . . .

Obsession: Radical Islam's War Against the West,
2005, advertisement.

The sensationalist film *Obsession*, produced by The Clarion Fund, poses as a documentary, warning viewers of "Radical Islam's War Against the West."

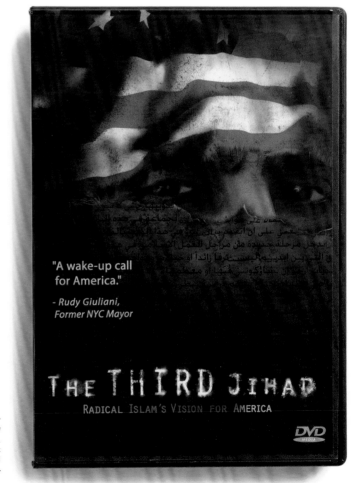

The Third Jihad: Radical Islam's Vision for America, *2008, DVD.*

The Clarion Fund also produced the 72-minute propaganda film *The Third Jihad*, which was screened before 1,500 New York City police officers as a part of an anti-terrorist training initiative. The narrator tells viewers that Muslims in the U.S. are a threat and hammers home the myth that Islam and terrorism are synonymous.

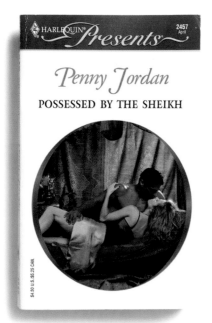

Possessed by the Sheikh,
2005, paperback book.

Romance novels featuring sheikhs
as objects of desire reinforce
romanticized notions of the Orient.

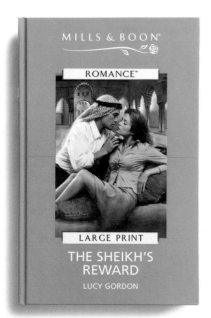

The Sheikh's Reward,
2000, paperback book.

is dark, but not black. He is Orientalized and . . . he is often a type of international playboy, with business and political interests all over the world."[15] But "the sheikh's country is often . . . backwards and needs modernizing." That's where the Western heroine steps in.[16]

There has been and continues to be plenty of racism with respect to Arabs and Muslims in Western spy thrillers that are set in and out of the Middle East. Not much has changed since John Buchan's novel *Greenmantle*. "Islam is a fighting creed," writes Buchan, "and the mullah stands in the pulpit with the Koran in one hand and a drawn sword in the other."[17] Since then, Arab demagogues, white slavers, religious fanatics, and terrorists have surfaced in more than 1,000 crime fiction and western thrillers. Several of the genre's successful writers — Daniel Silva, Vince Flynn, Joel C. Rosenberg, and Brad Thor — advance and solidify the stereotype by regularly depicting Arabs as religious fanatics moving to destroy the U.S., Israel, and other nations. Another long-lasting stereotype is that of the Palestinian as terrorist, which first surfaced in Thomas Harris's best-selling thriller *Black Sunday* (1975), which two years after its publication became a hit movie. Both the book and film focus on Palestinian terrorists attempting to kill the American president along with 80,000 people at a Super Bowl game.[18]

POST-9/11 TV DRAMAS Given the increased amount of time we spend watching television shows, the impact of insidious stereotypes is far greater nowadays. My collection contains dozens of TV dramas that were telecast on all the major networks — from CBS to Fox to NBC to Showtime — starting with the Fall 2002–2003 TV season. The networks created and began projecting a new, dangerous stereotype: Arab Americans and Muslim Americans as anti-American villains who relish killing their fellow Americans by blowing up people and buildings. This threatening stereotype — the Arab American and Muslim American Neighbor as Terrorist — warned viewers that America's own Arabs and Muslims (not to mention Arab foreigners) were intent on waging a holy war against America.

More than 60 programs have drilled this mythology into our living rooms. Images littered TV screens, advancing the myth that America's Muslims were running shadowy

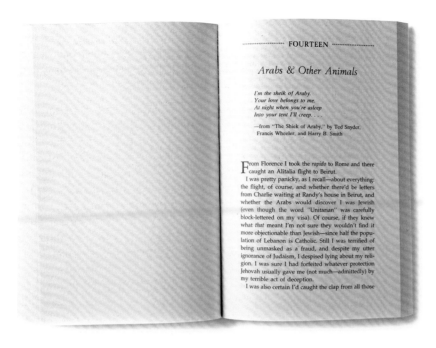

········· FOURTEEN ·········

Arabs & Other Animals

I'm the sheik of Araby.
Your love belongs to me.
At night when you're asleep
Into your tent I'll creep. . . .

—from "The Shiek of Araby," by Ted Snyder,
Francis Wheeler, and Harry B. Smith

From Florence I took the *rapido* to Rome and there caught an Alitalia flight to Beirut.

I was pretty panicky, as I recall—about everything: the flight, of course, and whether there'd be letters from Charlie waiting at Randy's house in Beirut, and whether the Arabs would discover I was Jewish (even though the word "Unitarian" was carefully block-lettered on my visa). Of course, if they knew what *that* meant I'm not sure they wouldn't find it more objectionable than Jewish—since half the population of Lebanon is Catholic. Still I was terrified of being unmasked as a fraud, and despite my utter ignorance of Judaism, I despised lying about my religion. I was sure I had forfeited whatever protection Jehovah usually gave me (not much—admittedly) by my terrible act of deception.

I was also certain I'd caught the clap from all those

Fear of Flying, *1973, paperback book.*

Helping to solidify the stale stereotype of Arab women as unattractive is Erica Jong's best-selling, feminist classic *Fear of Flying.* It contains a chapter entitled, "Arabs and Other Animals." Some of the slurs Jong uses to describe Arab women include: "…three ancient ladies in black (with gigantic bosoms and fuzzy mustaches)." And, "God — there's nothing to compare with being patted by a dozen two-hundred pound Lebanese women with mustaches." Though Jong now says that she regrets the chapter title, it appears even in the most recent version of *Fear of Flying.*

Jitterbug, *1984, paperback book.*

The book is set in the near future: Saudis rule the world and unleash a deadly virus. The West is controlled by Arab masters who perform mind control. Several of today's best-selling authors – Daniel Silva, Vince Flynn, and Brad Thor – regularly depict Arabs as religious fanatics moving to destroy the U.S., Israel, and other nations.

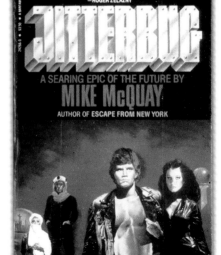

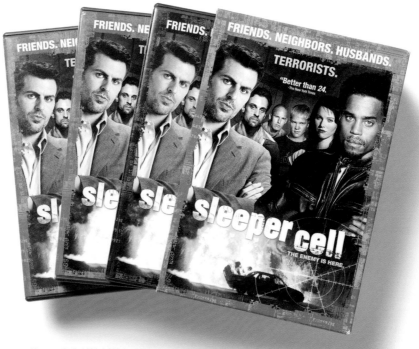

Sleeper Cell, *2005–6, DVD box set.*

Nominated for two Golden Globes during its two-year run, *Sleeper Cell* follows an undercover Muslim American FBI agent assigned to infiltrate a Muslim terrorist organization planning to attack the U.S. The Jack G. Shaheen Archive contains dozens of TV dramas like *Sleeper Cell, 24, The Unit, The Agency,* and *Threat Matrix* that were telecast on all the major networks beginning immediately after 9/11. These TV programs helped generate a serious backlash against Arab and Muslim Americans. They capitalized on post-9/11 fears and repeated negative images, reinforcing the myth that these communities are made up of religious radicals who merit profiling, imprisonment, torture, and death.

terrorist sleeper cells inside mosques from Los Angeles to Washington, DC. These TV programs helped generate a serious backlash against Arab Americans and Muslim Americans, punishing communities across the country. Several TV series — *24, Sleeper Cell, The Unit, NCIS, The Agency,* and *Threat Matrix* — capitalized on post-9/11 fears and repeated negative images over and over, pummeling home the myth that Muslim Americans and Arab Americans are religious radicals who merit profiling, imprisonment, torture, and death. Episodes of *The Practice, Judging Amy, The District, Covert Affairs, Law and Order* also displayed stock caricatures.

EDITORIAL CARTOONS For decades, editorial cartoonists have vilified Arabs. Among their attacks, cartoonists paint Palestinians as heartless terrorists who recruit their children to kill others as well as themselves, depict ostentatious

sheikhs taking over the U.S., and equate Arab leaders and peoples with animals such as rats. Images of decadent oil sheikhs proliferated in editorial cartoons in the 1970s and 1980s after Arab members of the Organization of Petroleum Countries (OPEC), an organization of Arab and non-Arab nations, declared an oil embargo against the U.S. in 1973. These depictions castigated Arabs as threats to the U.S. economy, identity, and lifestyle.

Editorial cartoonists continue to demean Arabs. Not much has changed since author Sam Keen addressed the National Association of Editorial Cartoonists gathering in San Diego, California on May 15, 1986. "You can hit an Arab free," Keen told the cartoonists. "They're free enemies, free villains — where you couldn't do it to a Jew and you can't do it to a black anymore."[19]

Berry's World, 1979, editorial cartoon.
Editorial cartoons from the 1970s–1990s depict Arabs controlling and manipulating the U.S. Here, an Arab is pictured winding up Uncle Sam.

Tony Auth, 2002, editorial cartoon.
Even Arab children are vilified by editorial cartoonists. These cartoons are especially scathing as they suggest that children are potential terrorists.

The Quigmans, 1993, editorial cartoon.

GOVERNMENT BUMPER STICKERS Instead of creating ads stressing energy conservation, in 1975, the U.S. government decided to come up with ads that blamed Arabs for all our energy woes. The Federal Energy Administration (FEA) printed and distributed 100,000 bumper stickers. One proclaimed, "The Faster You Drive, the Richer They Get," and another declared, "Driving 75 is Sheik, Driving 55 is Chic." In response to my inquiry requesting the two bumper stickers for my collection, FEA's Patrick F. Donnelly wrote to me on July 19, 1976, saying that all the bumper stickers had been recalled and that "only one could possibly be construed as Anti-Arab." I disagree.

The nature of prejudice; the Other; Arab/Jew Why is it important for the average American to know and care about

Federal Energy Administration bumper stickers, 1973.

Patrick F. Donnelly of the Federal Energy Administration (now the U.S. Department of Energy) responded to criticism by claiming "only one [of these bumper stickers] could possibly be construed as Anti-Arab."

the Arab stereotype? It is critical because the dislike of "the stranger," which the Greeks knew as xenophobia, forewarns that when one ethnic or racial or religious group is vilified, innocent people suffer. Popular culture's enemy Other is often projected as a complete "stranger" — a person outside the box whose color, culture, and creed is threateningly different. Usually, the Other boasts dark, unattractive, grotesque features: large noses and missing teeth. The Other needs a shower and a shave and dons non-Western garb: burnooses, head scarves, kufi hats, turbans, sombreros, and yarmulkes. The Other dwells in a primitive land without indoor plumbing: Africans in jungle huts, Asians and Latinos in shacks, Arabs and Native Americans in deserts or plain tents. The Other speaks broken English, complete with a thick accent. He or she is unattached to family. The Other believes in a different deity; he is anti-Christian. Functioning as a sexual predator, he kidnaps, holds hostage, and threatens to rape and kill Western white women. He is also a coward who never fights fair. Instead, the lurking-in-the-shadows Other sneaks up on and attacks the lone Western protagonist. The Other is inept in the bedroom and on the battlefield.

According to the mythology, the Other, especially Arabs, does not value human life as much as we do. The Arab demon of today is much like the Jewish demon of yesterday. Only now it wears a robe and headdress instead of a yarmulke and Star of David. Consider the image of Jews in pre-Nazi Germany. In the 1920s and 1930s, editorial cartoonists in Russia as well as Germany painted Jews as dark, shifty-eyed, venal, and threateningly different people.[20] After the Holocaust, the characterization of Jews as lecherous murderers or greedy financiers was no longer tolerable. Many cartoonists, however, reincarnated this caricature and transferred it to another group of Semites, the Arabs, portraying them as Shylocks in burnooses. Regrettably, it remains acceptable to keep

Driving 75 is sheik.
Driving 55 is chic.

Don't Be Fuelish

advancing anti-Semitism in popular culture provided that the Semites are Arabs. I encourage you, the reader, to examine the images displayed here; you will see that cartoonists painted Arabs and Jews with similar facial features; the so-called Jewish economic threat was linked to banking, the Arab threat to oil; both Jews and Arabs dressed differently and lusted after the pure, white virgin.

In the late 1980s, veteran filmmaker Ted Flicker spoke out against the Arab stereotype before the Boards of Directors of both the Writers Guild and Directors Guild in his speech, "Billionaires, Bombers and Belly Dancers." He said, "For those of us who remember what it was like to be Jewish in the '30s and '40s, stereotypes were part of the process that separated us from the rest of the American community. They were the cause of schoolyard fights and psychological scars that many of us carry today. . . . I think honor requires that we, the makers of our nation's myths, consider the plight of these people. . . .

My fellow writers. Help. Get rid of the Arab stereotype."[21]

President Bill Clinton best explains the importance of examining the Other's role in society, telling film critic Roger Ebert, "The biggest problem in human society is fear and distrust and dehumanization and violence against the Other. And that is a big problem. So, what we have to learn to do . . . is actively celebrate our differences. And the only way you can do that is to be secure in the knowledge that your common humanity is more important than your most significant differences." Adds Clinton, "And movies can help do that. That is really, really important."[22]

Conclusion Have we learned much from history? If so, why do some of us continue to fear and to hate those other people? It's the "Yellow Peril," warning us about the Yellow Asian horde, and it's the "Red Menace," perpetuating the myth that the dirty Communists are everywhere. And today, it's the "Green Menace," green being the color of Islam, and fear of 1.4 billion Muslims

TRUE CRIME HUNTING A KILLER IN L.A.

THE TRAGEDY OF **SARAH PALIN**

the Atlantic

Who Ruined Our Schools: An Insider Tells All
BY JOEL KLEIN

Is It Time To Dump U.S. Bonds?
BY MEGAN McARDLE

The Ultimate Guide To Hollywood
BY CLIVE JAMES

JUNE 2011
THEATLANTIC.COM

IS THIS THE FACE OF ARAB DEMOCRACY?

WHY THE NEW MIDDLE EAST IS MORE HOPEFUL— AND MORE HAZARDOUS
BY JEFFREY GOLDBERG

The Atlantic, *2011, magazine cover.*

This stereotypical image of an Arab woman stands in stark contrast to the vast majority of women participating in the Arab Spring movement. Furthermore, the cover's subtitle, "Why the New Middle East is More Hopeful — and More Hazardous," suggests that the recent democratic uprisings in the region should also be viewed as potentially dangerous and threatening. The image of the woman with only her eyes visible only further emphasizes the danger of the unknown/ unknowable Arab world.

and Arabs. Yet, I believe that eradicating this century-old stereotype may no longer be an insurmountable barrier. The Arab population of the Middle East is predicted to swell from its current 280 million to as high as 460 million by the year 2030. In many Arab countries, 70 percent of the population is under the age of 30 and an estimated 41 percent of Arabs are 14 and younger.

Here, and in the Middle East, thousands of young people like those involved in the Arab Spring movements will lead the way. We are witnessing Arab youth, women, and men seeking to take charge of their own affairs. They have even helped inspire people here in the U.S. to become involved with movements like Occupy Wall Street. Buffeted by pressure from various factions, pursuing democracy is a risk, but it is a risk young Arabs are taking. These young Arabs are painfully aware of the fact that the real work — addressing unemployment, health care, civil rights — begins after the protests subside and after the infighting and violence cease. The Arab Spring's organizers and participants know that democracy has never been easy, that it may take decades before stable governments will surface.

Contained in the Jack G. Shaheen Archive are motion pictures such as *Kingdom of Heaven* (2005); *The Visitor* (2007); *Amreeka* (2009); *Cairo Time* (2009); and *Fordson: Faith, Fasting, Football* (2011), an impressive documentary about Dearborn, Michigan's Arab American football team. Books, too, offer refreshing portraits. Check out Dave Eggers's nonfiction award-winner *Zeitoun,* about a Syrian American in New Orleans who rescues neighbors after Hurricane Katrina, and Diana Abu Jaber's beautifully written *Crescent* (2004), about Arab love, family, tradition, and cultural identity. Thanks to Naif Al-Mutawa's comic book series, *The 99*, young people here and abroad can read comic books featuring Arab and Muslim heroes. *The 99* comics have spawned an April 2011 PBS documentary *Wham! Bam! Islam!* and a forthcoming TV series — 26 half-hour animated episodes of *The 99* will be released in 2012 in more than 50 countries.

Television networks such as Turner Classic Movies (TCM) have taken positive steps to address the stereotype. I was the curator and guest expert along with host Robert

Osborne on the TCM series *Race and Hollywood: Arab Images on Film*, which aired in July 2011. Altogether, 32 features, five shorts, and several cartoons were telecast over eight days, presenting "Arabs as Villains," "Arabs as Subject of Ridicule," "Arabs as Sheiks," and so forth. In 2011, The Learning Channel's (TLC) critically-acclaimed *All-American Muslim* about five Muslim American families from Dearborn, Michigan, inspired a nationwide conversation about what it means to openly practice one's religion at a time when our perceptions of Arabs, Muslims, and Islam are at an all-time low. There was some concern that the reality series would be taken off the air when Lowe's, one of the show's main advertisers, pulled its commercials. Refreshingly, the show was not cancelled; advertising time for the remaining episodes had sold out, said a spokesperson for TLC.[23]

An increased presence of Arab Americans in the media has also increased the number of positive images available. Since 1996, my wife, Bernice, and I have awarded more than 50 academic scholarships to outstanding Arab American college students. Many of these scholars have gone on to leadership positions and are dispelling damaging images. Annemarie Jacir and Eyad Zahra, for example, produced and directed two acclaimed feature films, *Salt of this Sea* (2008) and *The Taqwacores* (2010). In 2007, Leila Fadel, another recipient, received the George Polk Award in Journalism for outstanding international reporting. Fadel, who currently covers the Middle East for the *Washington Post*, worked for McClatchy newspapers for several years as Baghdad bureau chief.

Prior to 9/11, there was a great deal of ignorance about Arabs, Muslims, and the Middle East. Since then, however, there has been an increased interest in the region, and Islam; more American students are learning Arabic and studying abroad in countries like Morocco, Tunisia, Egypt, Jordan, and Lebanon. The result, says my friend and colleague Dr. Larry Michalak, a Middle East specialist from the University of California, Berkeley, is a steady increase in American sophistication about the Middle East and the Muslim world, which is all to the good. The more we learn about Islam and the peoples of the region, the more we may alleviate and reject negative stereotypes. Regrettably, some politicians and special interest groups continue

16. Cover of a Swedish edition, Hangö, 1924

Forlaten Faller, *1924, book.*

The cover of *Forlaten Faller*, by Russian anti-Semitic mystic Sergei Nilus, shows the world being strangled by a snake with the head of a Jew. The "Arab Renaissance" cartoon plays on a similar theme, as an oil sheikh squeezes wealth from the rest of the world. Anti-Jewish and anti-Arab sentiments and policies share the same root of anti-Semitism.

The Spectator, *1979, editorial cartoon.*

New-found oil wealth has increased power behind Arab nationalism.

Three independent films offer refreshingly humane and compassionate portrayals of Arabs. Set in 2003, after the U.S. invades Iraq, *Amreeka* tells the story of a Palestinian mother and son trying to establish themselves in a new country. In *Salt of this Sea,* a Palestinian film, we follow an American-born Palestinian woman returning to her home. *The Visitor* offers portrayals of cross-cultural friendships amid the backdrop of post-9/11 deportation policies.

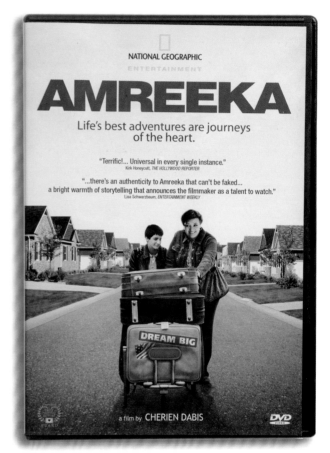

Amreeka, *2010, DVD.*

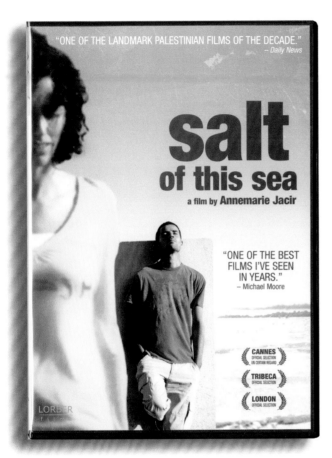

Salt of this Sea, *2010, DVD.*

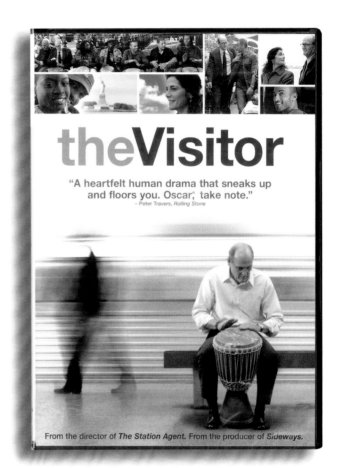

The Visitor, *2007, DVD.*

targeting Arabs and Muslims as "Islamofascists," a propaganda term used by some individuals who vilify Islam. Yet, there are many more ordinary American citizens, academics, image-makers, and religious leaders who are help-ing to humanize Arabs and educating the public about Islam.

I believe young scholars will play a significant role in the near future. They will build on the collection at New York University, my writings on the stereotype, the works of future scholars, and proceed to examine in greater depth the impact of popular culture's Arab and Muslim portraits. As Vaclav Havel, former President of the Czech Republic, points out in his book *The Art of the Impossible: Politics as Morality in Practice,* "None of us — as an individual — can save the world as a whole. . . . But each of us must behave as though it was in his power to do so."[24]

To some, dispensing with the Arab stereotype may seem an impossible task. Yet, openness to change is an American tradition and the strength of our society. Eventually, storytellers from Chicago to Cairo will project more honest images of Arabs, Muslims, and Americans with Arab roots — images that are no better and no worse than others. We will begin to see Arabs as neither saints nor devils, but as fellow human beings, with all the potentials and frailties that condition implies.

Together, these collectibles form the history of Arab portraits in U.S. popular culture and a labyrinthine matrix we are only now beginning to address. Yet, we should keep the faith! In time, damaging portraits will be shattered, image by image. Young scholars and artists will lead the way, creating inventive portraits that humanize the Arab.

The 99: Origins, *2007, comic book.*

Fair representations of Arabs and Muslims are possible. Though not produced in the U.S., *The 99* comic book series has inspired the PBS documentary *Wham! Bam! Islam!* and a forthcoming television series.

Beyond 9/11: Engaging with the Jack G. Shaheen Archive

Amita Manghnani

My father was on two episodes of *Hawaii Five-0*. In "The Ring of Life" (1975), he played an Indian consul named Badar Vasanti. The episode revolved around a British citizen's attempts to locate the fifth and final piece of the "Kashmiri Ring of Life," for which the Indian government had offered a million dollar reward. One review of the episode described his television debut as "amateurish," explaining, "English actor Harvey Jason as Ram Bushan, Indian government representative . . . seems more 'East Indian' than [Vasanti is]."[1] My father, apparently, could not outshine an actor in brown face. His second appearance on the series came in 1980, when he played oil sheikh Ahmed Bishara in "The School for Assassins." His character was in Honolulu for an Organization of the Petroleum Exporting Countries (OPEC) meeting, presumably representing one of the Gulf States.

As a child, I had always been told that the framed photograph of my father, whose face and neck were overgrown with beard, and whose head was adorned with a *ghutra* and *iqal*, was taken while he was preparing for his role as a terrorist on the famed Honolulu-based television series. I had accepted this explanation. The idea that a South Asian could play an Arab (who was obviously the show's resident terrorist and undoubtedly Muslim) seemed not only plausible, but

common sense in the 1990s, when movies like *True Lies* (1994) (produced with support from the Department of Defense and the U.S. Marine Corps Aviation)[2], *Patriot Games* (1992), and *Executive Decision* (1996) were selling out theaters across the country and portraying all olive-skinned, bearded men who appeared to be Arab, as violent, enraged threats.[3]

The Jack G. Shaheen Archive, recently acquired by New York University's Tamiment Library & Robert F. Wagner Labor Archives, places such onscreen portrayals within an extended legacy of anti-Arab and anti-Muslim representations. Providing a historical record of the representations of Arabs and Muslims in U.S. popular culture and media from the late-19th century to the present, the Shaheen Archive reveals their persistence and evolution. From images of the 1893 Chicago World's Fair, at which Little Egypt introduced Americans to belly dancing, to the wildly popular *Arabian Nights* (first translated into English in 1706), the Jack G. Shaheen Archive traces American Orientalism, revealing how embedded Islamophobia and anti-Arab sentiment are in our culture. The materials in the collection not only chronicle the perpetuation of images of the Arab and/or Muslim as "terrorist" or Arab and/or Muslim as "sheikh," but also expose the ideological and political work that they do.

Since the attacks on the World Trade Center and the Pentagon, the conflations between "Arab," "Muslim," and "South Asian" have intensified.[4] Several academics (Jasbir Puar, Junaid Rana, Leti Volpp, and Sunaina Maira, included) have identified September 11, 2001 as the moment at which peoples perceived to be "Arab" and/or "Muslim" are grouped together. In fact, many of the first hate crime victims in the days following September 11 were Sikh, including Balbir Singh Sodhi, the first post-9/11 hate crime murder victim.[5] Legal expert Leti Volpp writes,

> September 11 facilitated the consolidation of a new identity category that groups together persons who appear "Middle Eastern, Arab, or Muslim." This consolidation reflects a racialization wherein members of this group are identifiable terrorists, and are de-identified as citizens.[6]

If Arabs, Muslims, and South Asians can be "identified" as terrorists, what are the physical markers that make such identification possible? And how did these markers, which include dark skin, full beards, and non-Western dress consisting of long robes, turbans, and veils[7], come to be treated as indicators of terrorism? The understanding that people who "look Arab" or "look Muslim" are enemies to Western Civilization and a threat to the survival of the U.S. nation has been naturalized and perpetuated by the "War on Terror," which, for the last decade, has created an indiscriminate, overreaching geography of "terrorism" which now includes the South Asian nations of Afghanistan and Pakistan (crudely termed Af-Pak). Both de facto and de jure racial profiling (including the Patriot Act and the National Security Entry and National Security Entry-Exit Registration System [NSEERS] which was suspended on April 28, 2011[8]), as well as hate crimes against these populations have increased since 2001.

On Sunday, August 5, 2012, as this publication headed to press, six people were killed and three others wounded when an armed white supremacist attacked a Sikh *gurdwara* in Oak Creek, Wisconsin. Sikh American and South Asian American thinkers and organizations including Vijay Prashad, Amardeep

Singh, and the Sikh Coalition were quick to challenge the notion that this attack could be characterized as a case of "misrecognition." Perhaps Wade Michael Page thought his victims were Muslim, perhaps he knew they were Sikh. In the end, it was their racial difference that made them his targets. In the days following, a mosque in Joplin, Missouri was burned to the ground and mosques from North Smithfield, Rhode Island to Hayward, California were vandalized.

While recognizing September 11, 2001[9] as a critical moment in the racialization, "othering," and exclusion of Arabs, Muslims, and South Asians, it is important not to declare it the starting point for the demonization of these populations.[10] As Shaheen argues, the process to denigrate and dehumanize Arabs began not only well before the attacks on the World Trade Center but even before the U.S. had engaged in military interventions in the Arab world at all. The Jack G. Shaheen Archive, which largely consists of American mass media and popular culture images produced and disseminated pre-2001, makes this apparent, documenting a less-analyzed period of Arab and Muslim media representations.

Born in 1935 in Pittsburgh, Pennsylvania, Dr. Shaheen dedicated his career to identifying and contesting damaging stereotypes of Arabs and Muslims in American media. In the 1970s, after noticing racist images in his children's books, cartoons, and toys, he began collecting and cataloging these images with the help of his wife, Bernice Shaheen. Scouring issues of *TV Guide* for what he calls the "three b's" — belly dancers, bombers, and Bedouins — Shaheen recorded television programs, movies, advertisements, and news segments. He visited archives across the country to read movie reviews and screen films.

In and out of the university, Shaheen was met with resistance by those who refused to acknowledge the dangerous influence of Islamophobic and anti-Arab images, or the intellectual and academic significance of his work. Though he was often rejected by publishers and rebuffed by colleagues, Shaheen nevertheless managed to print editorials in publications like the *Wall Street Journal, Los Angeles Times, Boston Globe,* and

Washington Post all contesting the portrayals of Arabs and Muslims as the "other." Given that no other scholars or media critics were as publicly visible in challenging these images, Shaheen soon became the go-to expert on U.S. representations of Arabs and Muslims. He served as a consultant for films such as *Syriana* and *Three Kings*, and for the Los Angeles County Commission on Human Relations, the Department of Justice's Civil Rights Division, and New York City's Commission on Civil Rights.

Currently, Dr. Shaheen is a Distinguished Visiting Scholar at New York University's Asian/Pacific/American Institute and The Hagop Kevorkian Center for Near Eastern Studies. As a Graduate Archives Scholar at the Asian/Pacific/American Institute from 2009–11, I had the privilege of working with Dr. Shaheen and the Jack G. Shaheen Archive. The vilifying images and texts contained in the archive can be difficult to digest. And yet, the materials are invaluable. They reveal and document Western perceptions and understandings of the Middle East and its people over the course of centuries. They call attention to the ways that the stereotypes of Arabs and Muslims relate to the portrayals of other racialized peoples. They also demonstrate how demands for fair and realistic representations can be met with small, yet significant, changes. From history to film studies to ethnic studies, the possibilities for new scholarship and academic engagement with the materials in this collection are infinite, as is the potential to employ them as educational tools.

King Features, *1979, editorial cartoon.*
Contributing to the perception that Arabs were exploiting Americans' dependence on fuel, the editorial cartoon pictures three gleeful sheikhs singing "This Land Is Your Land."

The Re-Education of Jack Shaheen: Why the Shaheen Archive Is Important & What You Can Do to Help

John Kuo Wei Tchen, Director, A/P/A Institute, NYU

Jack Shaheen is a soft-spoken man on an extraordinary mission. He is the proud son of a Christian Lebanese family raised in a working class, multi-ethnic enclave of the Pittsburgh steel mills.

He was the first Shaheen to go to college and gain a Ph.D. The mass communications assistant professorship at Southern Illinois University meant he could rise from the horizon of the factory floor. His early academic trajectory indicates he was well on his way towards academic security and success. In the burgeoning field of media studies, he had written a timely book on nuclear war films, essays on the newly formed Public Broadcasting Service (PBS), and an essay on Jacque Cousteau's documentation of the yet little-known underworld of the ocean's life. With a Ph.D., his partner Bernice, and two young children in the heartland of America, life was good. A house with a lawn, a car paid for on the installment plan . . . It was an American Dream come true.

But Jack's personal and professional path was about to change. At the center of the new mass communications revolution was television. This medium brought a world of stories into the family's living space. Silly, playful cartoons beamed catchy, racist caricatures through the impressionable eyes and ears of Shaheen's children, Michael and Michele, piercing their parents' hearts and minds. Bugs, Woody, and Popeye had bombarded generations of families, and racial typecasting still flourished. These were toxic tales. Michael and Michele were raised to be proud of their Arab American heritage, and this assault splintered their youthful naiveté with doubts about who they were and where their world stood in the scheme of the larger outside.

The cartoons referenced enough "Arab" stereotypes for young children to absorb and cause a dis-affiliation. The animated protagonist was fighting the evil Arab villain. In this mediated process, one's self-image becomes split. *We're not bad like the bad guys. We're good like the good guys.* These strange, anti-Arab/anti-Muslim images spread like a virus through the airwaves into Middle America, spreading to all within the body politic.

> *The recovery of these dehumanizing fragments into one archival space enables those who want to see the pattern, to see and to understand.*

Once the Shaheen family became aware of such offenses, it became increasingly clear such toxic stories were all around. Once they became aware, they began noticing how saturated the culture was with the American fetish for Arab-exotica: the costumes at Halloween parties, toys at the local mall, jokes told in passing, *Weekly Readers*, ad nauseum.

Doubt and stigma, what Philip Roth called "the human stain," could have seriously eroded the Shaheens' sense of self-worth. Yet, the family recognized both the fallacy and power of these representations, and they did what few families would do. They began collecting and describing each instance of Arab stereotyping they found. Rather than remaining passive spectators, they became active documentarians. The family and a network of friends countered this constant assault on their self-image. In that process, they made their personal antipathy more substantive, more real. They became active agents in fighting what was wrong.

Michael and Michele could have responded in one of at least two ways. And so could have Jack and Bernice. In the face of this onslaught, the Shaheen children could have each become oblivious and non-communicative of the viral meme's effect on them, swallowing their sense of self-worth without thinking and without saying something to each other or to their parents. Instead, they voiced their feelings in order to ward off these powerful messages. Yet, the question remains, even while fending off such assaults, did these negative messages erode and cast doubt about these children's place in the world? And, as if not more important, what values do non-"bad" Arabs/Muslims grow up with?

The Shaheen parents could have responded by clamping down on what the children could watch or forbade the watching of children's cartoons or television altogether. Given Jack's love of the movies and work in mass communications, this was not an option. Instead, the family as a whole came together to talk, to collect, and to analyze what was going on.

This was the beginning of the re-education of Jack Shaheen, a Ph.D.'d scholar. Whatever theories and paradigms he had learned and mastered as a graduate student did not prepare him for these real-life issues. Writing of another time and another group, sociologist W.E.B. Du Bois can help us understand what was going on. For those deemed "others," the mass culture of good whites and bad "others" caused a split in self-awareness. Writing in 1903, Du Bois wrote, in *The Souls of Black Folk*, of the African American dilemma, especially in the South. "The Negro" subjected to "a world which yields him no true self-consciousness, but only lets him see himself through the revelation of the other [the white] world. It is a peculiar sensation, this double-consciousness, this sense of always looking at one's self through the eyes of others, of measuring one's soul by the tape of a world that looks on in amused contempt and pity."

The prevailing academic practice of research and writing being disengaged and "objective," were now put through the test of real life. This was up close and personal. To take what happened seriously, required Jack Shaheen to cross a tabooed no man's zone into uncharted territory that would risk his career.

Jack Shaheen writes that soon after first identifying troubling images in his children's Saturday morning cartoons, his proposal to make such images the subject of his research changed how his academic colleagues perceived and treated him. Suddenly, he was stigmatized as the "Arab professor" and turned down for research grants. He was criticized as promoting "Arab propaganda." Up until this point, Jack had not consciously experienced the sting of personal racism. He was 40 years old and had had much success. Shaheen's trials and tribulations in publishing *The TV Arab* (1984) manuscript further pushed him to understand his experiences in a broader context. After many letters of rejection, it became clear the intellectual establishment did not want to deal with this issue. It is such moments of clarity that mark the pathways in which all Americans, sooner or later, in one way or another, become stained with the taint of racial classification. This rude moment changed the course and quality of his life's work.

In this sobering coming-to-awareness process, the anti-racist foundations of the Jack G. Shaheen Archive were laid. He wrote op-ed pieces. Many were rejected. Some were published. Essay by essay, he brought these questions to public attention. Some appreciated this lone voice in the media desert. After decades of collecting and documenting the U.S. media industry, that 1970s jolt of being racially typecast has produced two definitive, painstaking studies: *Reel Bad Arabs: How Hollywood Vilifies a People* (2001) and *Guilty: Hollywood's Verdict on Arabs After 9/11* (2008).

Tested by decades of battle in the crucible of the heartland of the U.S. – those who want to believe patriotism is "America right or wrong," "love it or leave it" – Jack Shaheen has, with little rhetoric and little fanfare, exposed, show by show, film by film, advertisement by advertisement, toy by toy, irrefutable evidence of culture-wide, systemic stereotyping. The patterns are cumulative, overwhelming, and undeniable.

The Jack G. Shaheen Archive at the Tamiment Library & Robert F. Wagner Labor Archives at NYU, containing over 4,000 items, has now transformed *the possibility* of public understanding. Rather than appreciating his books as simply a measure of personal, professional accomplishment (which they are) and his donated archive as the research notes and files for the writing of his books (which it is), we need to also recognize a more important accomplishment.

The Shaheen Archive has, case by case, challenged the silence and obliviousness of U.S. popular culture. It exposes a pattern of self-perpetuating stereotyping of a whole people in the world and in the U.S. This archive has opened up a space of light and air to look into and to understand what is and what has been going on. The recovery of these dehumanizing fragments – fragments that have been so pervasive we hadn't truly noticed them – into one archival space enables those who want to see the pattern, to see and to understand. *The emperor has no clothes!*

Archives are a bit mysterious for those who don't use them. So allow me to elaborate what the Shaheen Archive does:

1. This archive is a physical collection that opens up a cultural space for research, reflection, and use. It is open to all.

2. This archive is part of a process of diagnosis and dialogue. The harm perpetuated by systemic misrepresentation can and must be combated to begin a healing process.

3. This archive needs to grow and become even more definitive. We need to collect more for it. Additional collections need to be alongside it.

4. This archive is an investment in the future.

> *We have to grow this collection, add additional collections, and build an even more irrefutable archive.*

The Jack G. Shaheen Archive has transformed a family's personal dilemma into an archival research space, social and open, inviting cross-cultural understanding and promoting rigorous scholarship. What one man, what one couple, what one family has done has had a generative multiplier effect.

Yet, this is not enough. This is just a foundational beginning. We have to grow this collection, add additional collections, and build an even more irrefutable archive. Rather than waiting for whole systems of education and perpetrators of this popular propaganda to "see the light," we can begin with the everyday research, writing, documentation, and creative work we do. The possibility of more people understanding is still only that – a possibility. We have to maximize that possibility until it becomes part of our culture's common understanding of our common humanity.

Join us in building this archive!

Endnotes

"A is for Arab"

1. Walter Lippmann, *Public Opinion* (New York: Harcourt, Brace and Company, Inc., 1922), 90. Lippmann himself was not immune to what he warned about. In a Feb. 13, 1942 piece in the *Los Angeles Times* titled "The Fifth Column," he favored the removal of Japanese Americans from the Pacific coast and wanted Washington, DC "to adopt a policy of mass evacuation and mass internment of all those who are technically enemy aliens."

2. Charles Haberl, personal correspondence with the author, March 9, 2012.

3. Edward Said, *Orientalism* (New York: Pantheon, 1978), 125.

4. "Facts About Islam," American-Arab Anti-Discrimination Committee, accessed May 24, 2012, http://www.adc.org/education/facts-about-islam/.

5. Janet Smith, "Anti-Muslim Hate Crime Rash," Southern Poverty Law Center, September 16, 2011, http://www.splcenter.org/blog/2011/09/16/anti-muslim-hate-crime-rash-reputed-around-911-date.

6. Stacy Takacs, *Terrorism TV: Popular Entertainment in Post-9/11 America* (Lawrence: University Press of Kansas, 2012), 23.

7. Gabriel Elizondo, "No bitterness 10 years after Sikh killing over 9/11," *Al Jazeera,* September 6, 2011, http://blogs.aljazeera.net/americas/2011/09/06/no-bitterness-10-years-after-sikh-killing-over-911.

8. Edward R. Murrow, "Keynote Address to the Radio and Television News Directors Association" (Chicago, Illinois, October 15, 1958). It should be noted that, as with Walter Lippmann, Murrow was not without his own moments of xenophobia. In Roger Daniel's *Prisoners Without Trial* (2004) Murrow is quoted as saying the following at a 1942 talk referencing Japanese Americans: "I think that if Seattle does get bombed you will be able to look up and see University of Washington sweaters on the Japanese boys doing the bombing" (38).

9. Matt Warman, "Average video gamer is 37," *The Telegraph,* June 8, 2011, http://www.telegraph.co.uk/technology/video-games/8564342/Average-video-gamer-is-37.html.

10. Gaylord Dubois, *Blaze Brandon with the Foreign Legion* (Wisconsin: Whitman Publishing, 1938), 94.

11. "It's Racist, but Hey, It's Disney," *New York Times,* July 14, 1993.

12. Lynette Rice,"'Aladdin' Sequel Draws Complaints from Arab-American committee," *Los Angeles Times,* May19,1994, 25.

13. Sana Venjara, "'The Third Jihad' and New York City's Culture of Marginalization," *Next American City,* January 27, 2012, http://americancity.org/buzz/entry/3290.

14. Sixty percent of Americans have never met a Muslim and some Arab and Muslim communities in our country believe they are treated with unfair suspicion and are unjustly targeted by law enforcement agencies. To help dispel such anxieties in New York, the mayor should make available to NYPD members knowledgeable speakers who specialize in Arab and Islamic studies; they should be invited to address members of the NYPD to discuss stereotypes presented by *The Third Jihad,* followed by much-needed dialogues between local Arabs and Muslims, the police, and other civil servants. The ultimate goal of such a productive dialogue would be to help shatter harmful myths and bring about better understanding between law enforcement officers and their respective communities. See Faiza Patel's, *Rethinking Radicalization,* Brennan Center For Justice at New York University School of Law, 2011. Officials should heed the wisdom of Hillary Clinton, who reminded us, while speaking at a 1996 White House prayer breakfast, that: "The vast majority of Arabs and Muslims in the United States are loyal citizens. [Their] daily lives revolve around work, family, and community. . . . It's not fair to apply a negative stereotype to all [Arabs and] Muslims." Not fair, indeed.

15. Jessica Taylor, "And You Can Be My Sheikh: Gender, Race, and Orientalism in Contemporary Romance Novels," *The Journal of Popular Culture,* 40 (2007): 1042.

16. Ibid.,1046.

17. John Buchan, *Greenmantle* (London: Hodder & Stoughton, 1916), 18.

18. More than one thousand Arab villains appear in spy novels; see Reeva Simon's telling books, *The Middle East in Crime Fiction: Mysteries, Spy Novels, and Thrillers From 1916 to the 1980s* (1989) and *Spies and Holy Wars* (2011). Simon calls our attention to hundreds of published books that feature heroic soldiers; civilians; special Israeli, American, and European agents; and others eradicating scores of Arab villains.

19. My notes from Keen's address to the National Association of Editorial Cartoonists gathering in San Diego, California, May 15, 1986; see Keen's book, *Faces of the Enemy,* 1986, 29–30.

20. For additional reading see Jonathan Freedman, *Klezmer America: Jewishness, Ethnicity, Modernity* (2009) and Sander Gilman, *Multiculturalism and the Jews* (2006).

21. Flicker's comments are cited in Casey Kasem's essay, "Arab Defamation in the Media: Its Consequences and Solutions," published in *The Link,* Vol. 23, No. 5, December 1990. After Kasem introduced me to Flicker, he helped convince him to take a stand on the stereotype. At the time, he and Flicker were participating in an Arab-Jewish dialogue on conflict resolution.

22. President Clinton's comments were made to film critic Roger Ebert on his weekly film program, *Roger Ebert and the Movies,* UPN-TV, February 28, 2000.

23. Alan Duke, "'All American Muslim' Sells Out, Despite Lowe's Withdrawal," *CNN,* December 13, 2011, http://articles.cnn.com/2011-12-13/entertainment/showbiz_american-muslim-tv-ads_1_ad-time-russell-simmons-unsold-commercial-time?_s=PM:SHOWBIZ.

24. David Holley, "Vaclav Havel dies at 75; Czech leader of '89 'Velvet Revolution,'" *Los Angeles Times,* December 18, 2011, accessed May 25, 2012, http://articles.latimes.com/2011/dec/18/local/la-me-1219-vaclav-havel-20111219-5.

Beyond 9/11

1. Mike Quigley, "Five-O Oddities, Goofs, Trivia – Season 7," accessed March 2, 2011, http://www.mjq.net/fiveo/5-0log7.htm.

2. Jack Shaheen, *Reel Bad Arabs: How Hollywood Vilifies a People*, rev. ed. (New York: Olive Branch Press, 2009), 535-6.

3. Amaney Jamal and Nadine Naber, eds., *Race and Arab Americans Before and After 9/11: From Invisible Citizens to Visible Subjects* (Syracuse: Syracuse University Press, 2007), 37.

4. Ibid., 2.

5. Dawinder S. Sidhu and Neha Singh Gohil, *Civil Rights in Wartime: The Post-9/11 Sikh Experience* (London: Ashgate Publishing, 2009), 189.

6. Leti Volpp, "Citizen and the Terrorist," *UCLA Law Review* 49 (2001-2): 1576.

7. Jack Shaheen, *Guilty: Hollywood's Verdict on Arabs after 9/11* (New York: Olive Branch Press, 2008), 7.

8. Channing Kennedy, "After Nine Years of Pressure, DHS Finally Drops 'SB1070 for Muslims,'" *Colorlines,* April 29, 2011, accessed May 1, 2011, http://colorlines.com/archives/2011/04/after_nine_years_of_pressure_dhs_finally_drops_its_sb1070_for_muslims.html.

9. William Rubenstein, "The Real Story of U.S. Hate Crimes Statistics: An Empirical Analysis," *Tulane Law Review* 78 (2003-4): 1234.

10. Jamal and Naber, 4.

Jack G. Shaheen Publications

"American Television: Arabs in Dehumanizing Roles." In *The American Media and the Arabs*, edited by Michael C. Hudson and Ronald G. Wolfe, 39–44. Washington, DC: Center for Contemporary Arab Studies, Georgetown University, 1980.

"The Arab Image in American Mass Media." *American-Arab Affairs* 2 (1982): 89–96.

"The Arab Image in American Mass Media." In *Split Vision: The Portrayal of Arabs in the American Media*, edited by Edmund Ghareeb, 327–36. Washington, DC: American-Arab Affairs Council, 1983.

"The Arab: TV's Most Popular Villain." *The Christian Century* 95 (1978): 1213–15.

"Arabs – TV's Villains of Choice." *Channels of Communication* 4 (1984): 52–53.

"The Arabs and the Moviemakers." *Middle East International (G.B.)* 238 (1984): 15–16.

"The Arab Stereotype on Television." *The Link* 13 (1980): 1–3.

"'Ashanti': The Arab as Black Slaver." *Middle East Perspective* 12 (1979): 4–5.

"Do Television Programs Stereotype the Arabs?" *Wall Street Journal*, October 12, 1979, S:10.

Guilty: Hollywood's Verdict on Arabs after 9/11. New York: Olive Branch Press, 2008.

"The Influence of the Arab Stereotype on American Children." *Arab Perspectives* 1 (1980):15–20.

"Movie Arabs: Why the Stereotypes?" *Arab Perspectives* 5 (1984): 27–30.

"On Prejudice: A Review of Arab Images." *Arab Perspectives* 4 (1983): 22–27.

Reel Bad Arabs: How Hollywood Vilifies a People, rev. ed. New York: Olive Branch Press, 2009.

"A Skewed Image of Arabs." *Christian Science Monitor*, September 17, 1990.

The TV Arab. Bowling Green, Ohio: Bowling Green State University Popular Press, 1984.

"TV Pictures in Our Mind." *The Medium* 1 (1982): 2–4.

"TV's Dehumanizing Perception of Arabs." *The Media Reporter (G.B.)* 4 (1980): 38–39.

"The Ugly Arabs: U.S. TV Image." *Middle East (G.B.)* 43 (1978): 108–10.

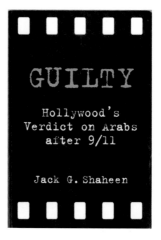

Guilty: Hollywood's Verdict on Arabs After 9/11,
2008, paperback book.

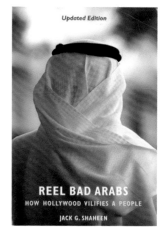

Reel Bad Arabs: How Hollywood Vilifies a People,
2009, paperback book.

Selected Bibliography

American-Arab Anti-Discrimination Committee. "Facts About Islam." Accessed May 24, 2012. http://www.adc.org/education/facts-about-islam/.

Barnouw, Erik. *The Sponsor: Notes on a Modern Potentate*. New York: Oxford University Press, 1978.

Bradley, Barbara. "Toy Companies Ride Military Wave and Watch Kids Catch It." *Christian Science Monitor*, December 10, 1986. http://www.csmonitor.com/1986/1210/atoys-f.html.

Buchan, John. *Greenmantle*. London: Hodder & Stoughton, 1916.

Daniels, Roger. *Prisoners Without Trial*. New York: Hill and Wang, 2004.

Dubois, Gaylord. *Blaze Brandon with the Foreign Legion*. Wisconsin: Whitman Publishing, 1938.

Du Bois, W. E. B. *The Souls of Black Folk*. New York: Arc Manor LLC, (1903) 2008.

Duke, Alan. "'All American Muslim' Sells Out, Despite Lowe's Withdrawal." *CNN,* December 13, 2011. http://articles.cnn.com/2011-12-13/entertainment/showbiz_american-muslim-tv-ads_1_ad-time-russell-simmons-unsold-commercial-time?_s=PM:SHOWBIZ.

Elizondo, Gabriel. "No bitterness 10 years after Sikh killing over 9/11," *Al Jazeera*, September 6, 2011. http://blogs.aljazeera.net/americas/2011/09/06/no-bitterness-10-years-after-sikh-killing-over-911.

Freedman, Jonathan. *Klezmer America: Jewishness, Ethnicity, Modernity*. New York: Columbia University Press, 2009.

Gilman, Sander. *Multiculturalism and the Jews*. New York: Routledge, 2006.

Greenfield, Meg. "Our Ugly Arab Complex," *Newsweek,* December 5, 1977.

Havel, Vaclav. *The Art of the Impossible: Politics as Morality in Practice*. New York: Knopf, 1997.

Holley, David. "Vaclav Havel dies at 75; Czech leader of '89 'Velvet Revolution.'" *Los Angeles Times*, December 18, 2011. Accessed May 25, 2012. http://articles.latimes.com/2011/dec/18/local/la-me-1219-vaclav-havel-20111219-5.

Huxley, Aldous. *The Olive Tree*. London: Chatto & Windus, 1936.

"It's Racist, but Hey, It's Disney," *New York Times,* July 14, 1993.

Jamal, Amaney, and Nadine Naber, eds. *Race and Arab Americans Before and After 9/11: From Invisible Citizens to Visible Subjects*. Syracuse: Syracuse University Press, 2007.

Kasem, Casey. "Arab Defamation in the Media: Its Consequences and Solutions." *The Link* 23 (1990).

Keen, Sam. *Faces of the Enemy*. San Francisco: Harper & Row, 1986.

Kennedy, Channing. "After Nine Years of Pressure, DHS Finally Drops 'SB1070 for Muslims,'" *Colorlines*, April 29, 2011. Accessed May 1, 2011. http://colorlines.com/archives/2011/04/after_nine_years_of_pressure_dhs_finally_drops_its_sb1070_for_muslims.html.

Lippmann, Walter. *Public Opinion*. New York: Harcourt, Brace and Company, Inc., 1922.

Murrow, Edward R. "Keynote Address to the Radio and Television News Directors Association." Chicago, Illinois, October 15, 1958.

New York Advisory Committee to the United States Commission on Civil Rights. *Civil Rights Implications of Post-September 11 Law Enforcement Practices in New York*. CR1.2:2004/024309. Washington, DC, March 2004. http://www.usccr.gov/pubs/sac/ny0304/ny0304.pdf.

Patel, Faiza. *Rethinking Radicalization.* New York: Brennan Center For Justice at New York University School of Law, 2011.

Quigley, Mike. "Five-O Oddities, Goofs, Trivia – Season 7." Accessed March 2, 2011. http://www.mjq.net/fiveo/5-0log7.htm.

Rice, Lynette. "'Aladdin' Sequel Draws Complaints from Arab-American Committee." *Los Angeles Times,* May 19, 1994.

Roger Ebert and the Movies. UPN-TV, February 28, 2000.

Rubenstein, William. "The Real Story of U.S. Hate Crimes Statistics: An Empirical Analysis." *Tulane Law Review* 78 (2003–4): 1234.

Said, Edward. *Orientalism.* New York: Pantheon, 1978.

Shohat, Ella. "Gender in Hollywood's Orient." *Middle East Report* 162 (1990): 40-42.

—— "Gender and the Culture of Empire: Toward a Feminist Ethnography of the Cinema." *Quarterly Review of Film and Video* 131 (1991): 4584.

Shohat, Ella and Richard Porton, "The Trouble with Hanna: Costa Gavras and the Representation of Palestine." *Film Quarterly* (198485): 5055.

Sidhu, Dawinder S., and Neha Singh Gohil. *Civil Rights in Wartime: The Post-9/11 Sikh Experience.* London: Ashgate Publishing, 2009.

Simon, Reeva. *The Middle East in Crime Fiction: Mysteries, Spy Novels, and Thrillers From 1916 to the 1980s.* New York: Lilian Barber Press, Inc., 1989.

—— *Spies and Holy Wars.* Austin: University of Texas Press, 2011.

Smith, Janet. "Anti-Muslim Hate Crime Rash." Southern Poverty Law Center, September 16, 2011. http://www.splcenter.org/blog/2011/09/16/anti-muslim-hate-crime-rash-reported-around-911-date/.

Takacs, Stacy. *Terrorism TV: Popular Entertainment in Post-9/11 America.* Lawrence: University Press of Kansas, 2012.

Taylor, Jessica. "And You Can Be My Sheikh: Gender, Race, and Orientalism in Contemporary Romance Novels." *The Journal of Popular Culture* 40 (2007): 1032–1051.

Turan, Kenneth. "Saudi Shoot-'em-up." *The Los Angeles Times*, September 28, 2007.

Venjara, Sana. "'The Third Jihad' and New York City's Culture of Marginalization." *Next American City*, January 27, 2012. http://americancity.org/buzz/entry/3290/.

Volpp, Leti. "Citizen and the Terrorist," *UCLA Law Review* 49 (2001–2): 1575–1600.

Warman, Matt. "Average video gamer is 37." *The Telegraph*, June 8, 2011, http://www.telegraph.co.uk/technology/video-games/8564342/Average-video-gamer-is-37.html.

Woll, Allen and Randall Miller. *Ethnic and Racial Images in American Film and Television: Historical Essays and Bibliography.* New York: Garland Publishing, 1987.

Acknowledgments from Jack Shaheen

I am eternally grateful to my dear wife, Bernice. From the very beginning, she was always there to assist me as I struggled to legitimize the study of the Arab stereotype, to prove that it was as injurious as other stereotypes. During this time, I was swimming upstream with little or no help from anyone except for her. Bernice's incisive editing skills, love, and encouragement were instrumental in making my writings and collection possible. Thank you, and God Bless you, dear Bernice.

I wish to express heartfelt thanks to my good friend, Professor Jack Tchen, who first acknowledged the importance of my research and who encouraged me to donate my collection to New York University. Thanks to his vision, expertise, kindness, sensitivity, and friendship, the collection will forever be available to assist students and scholars world-wide in their studies of the Middle East, stereotypes, and the politics of representation. I am also forever grateful to an outstanding young scholar, Amita Manghnani, for her invaluable, ongoing assistance. Amita's dedication, tireless work, and creative thinking helped make this booklet and the accompanying *A is for Arab* exhibition possible. And special thanks to Ali Mirsepassi and Ella Shohat for their contributions.

I also wish to thank, for their continuous encouragement, my New York University friends and colleagues, Dr. Michael Gilsenan, Professor of Middle Eastern and Islamic Studies; and Greta Scharnweber, the Hagop Kevorkian Center for Near Eastern Studies' Associate Director. The late Dr. Michael H. Nash (1946—2012), head of the Tamiment Library & Robert F. Wagner Labor Archives, played an instrumental role in establishing the Jack G. Shaheen Archive at NYU. I will always be grateful for his vision and commitment. I received much moral support from Peter Magierski, Middle East Studies Librarian at NYU Libraries. I also thank Laura Chen-Schultz for her innovative production skills; she and her colleagues at the Asian/Pacific/American Institute were always available to lend a helping hand.

Finally, I thank my family members, friends, and colleagues who over the years called my attention to collectibles I might otherwise have missed.